Copyright © 2020 by Jannette Q
21 Crows, LLC

Little Book of Gettysburg Ghosts

ISBN: 978-1-940087-42-9

21 Crows Dusk to Dawn Publishing, 21 Crows, LLC

All rights reserved. No part of this book may be reproduced or transmitted in any form or by any means, electronic or mechanical, including photocopying, recording, or by any information storage and retrieval system, without permission in writing from the copyright owner. This is a work of fiction. Names, characters, places and incidents either are the product of the author's imagination or are used fictitiously, and any resemblance to any actual persons, living or dead, events, or locales is entirely coincidental. This book was printed in the United States of America.

Disclaimer: The stories and legends in this book are for enjoyment purposes and taken from many different resources. Many have been passed down and have been altered along the way. I attempt to sort through the many different variations found on a story and find the most popular and the most supported by historical evidence/verbal interviews. Not all sources and legends can be substantiated. Public properties may become private after the printing of the book or they may simply be listed with the address so you know the historical area where the story originated. Listing the GPS and address does not mean you can visit. Regardless if the area is listed as private or not, please respect the landowner and do not disturb their privacy, nor trespass. Readers assume full responsibility for use of information in this book. Please use common sense.

Cover Art:
Brenda Neuroth—ALLVISIONSART
Ractapopulous
Artycrafter

The Battle of Gettysburg
and the spirits that came after—

During the Battle of Gettysburg—Pickett's Charge.
Library of Congress

Being one of the biggest and bloodiest battles of the Civil War, there are hundreds and hundreds of new and old stories, historical books and articles, blogs, and websites to peruse for information about almost every battle and fight that go into great depth and detail. Many differ according to information passed down by lips or personal diaries or sides chosen to support.

I give just a taste of the history to help my readers get a feel for the legend surrounding a story and many times in the context of whatever side of the battle held the lore, north or south. In the back of the book, I have left notes of the trail I followed to find the story as citations. Many are worth following up on if you love to take bigger bites of history. Some are so exciting that I found myself diving into for hours at a time, and I'm surprised I got this book finished because of them.

The American Civil War was violent and horrific and bloody. From 1861 to 1865, it was fought by the passionate, the indifferent, the rich, the poor, the young, and the old in 10,000 places with the loss of over 620,000 soldiers. It had magnificent triumphs and grand defeats, kindhearted deeds, and horrid cruelties. Battles raged in the frigid winter mountains of West Virginia to a scorching prairie in Texas. One stands out as the bloodiest—the Battle of Gettysburg.

Right after the battle—View from Cemetery Hill with the town of Gettysburg in background. *Library of Congress*

In the summer of 1863, Confederate Robert E. Lee launched his second invasion into the northern states. In the wake and not on accident, two armies fiercely collided in the orchards, farmland, and even within the town of Gettysburg. It was July 1st through July 3rd, to be exact when soldiers from the North and the South came face to face beneath cloudy skies and 80-degree weather right smack dab in the thriving community of Gettysburg. At the end of those three days, there were about 8,000 soldiers killed. In the aftermath and well over a century and a half later, you can't toss a stone standing in the middle of town and not hit something filled with ghostly energy.

The Jennie Wade Museum
(McClellan House)
548 Baltimore St
Gettysburg, PA 17325
39.823334, -77.230693

Buried with Flour Still on Her Hands— The Tragic Story of Jennie Wade

In 1863, the divided states were two years into the American Civil War and working into the third. There was always the looming fear that a battle would show up at any town's front door or that enemy raiders would slip into a community to loot local stores and steal horses. The threat seemed an even greater certainty in the summer of that year for those who lived in Gettysburg. They were on the threshold of General Lee's invasion of the North. On June 24th, the Confederate Army crossed the Potomac River just around the corner and headed into Pennsylvania.

A hometown view of Gettysburg north—1863, picket fences, gardens, and white wood houses. *Library of Congress—Tyson Brothers.*

Word quickly traveled that soldiers were in Chambersburg, then after Carlisle and Harrisburg. Pennsylvania was a Union State. Most of those living in the town were northern supporters and many of their young men had joined the Union forces earlier in the war. The city was a thriving community of 2,400 citizens with over forty businesses including a college, taverns and banks, shoemakers, butcher shops, a carriage manufacturer, and tanneries. The network of roads intersecting the town and its fertile farming fields from the north and south, which had placed it as a prime location for industry, was also the system of roads the armies would take into their county.

The townspeople had been cautioned. Earlier in the spring, a telegram came from the governor asserting the storekeepers in Gettysburg should take precautions and move their businesses to a safer location. The warning proved faithful. After cries in the streets that the rebels were coming, the Confederate infantry poured through Gettysburg on June 26th on their way to Hanover Junction and York. The raggedy-dressed soldiers ransacked the stores and homes for anything they could carry; the officers demanded flour, groceries, clothing, shoes, whiskey, and money.

Confederate soldiers in Gettysburg. *Library of Congress.*

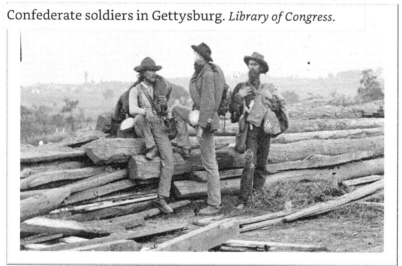

Most of the residents of Gettysburg had fled from the impending onslaught of a war raging right in their backyards. It was a soggy affair, and the roads were muddy beneath carriage wheels and horse hooves. It had been raining intermittently; the drab sky was a dark hue, which probably didn't help with the mood and the grim task of packing what little belongings they could in a hurry. It was on the cusp of a full moon, and all those superstitions surrounding it, pleasant or wicked, played on many minds.

Some had left, but not all. One, in particular, was a 20-year-old seamstress Virginia "Jennie" Wade—barely 5-feet-tall with long, dark hair. She was still tarrying in the clapboard home she shared with her small family on Breckenridge Street that included her mother, 43-year-old Mary Ann, 17-year-old James "Jack", who had entered the Union Army, 12-year-old Samuel, who boarded at the butcher shop where he worked as a hired hand, and 8-year-old Harry.

Georgeanna McClellan (Wade), Maria Comfort (neighborhood friend), and Jennie Wade. Daguerreotype by Speaits, Gettysburg 1861—From A True Story of Jennie Wade—A Gettysburg Maid

Mary Virginia Wade was born on May 21, 1843, in Gettysburg. She was also called Ginnie, but an inaccurate misprint from newspaper clippings has left her to be known as *Jennie.*

Jennie was watching Harry, and also 6-year-old Isaac Brinkerhoff, a boarder who was unable to walk and whose working mother paid the family to babysit. Her mother was a few blocks away, helping Jennie's 22-year-old sister, Georgia (Wade) McClellan, with a son born only a few days earlier and just hours before the Confederates came to town. Georgia's husband, a carpenter by trade, was away at the time as a private in the 165th Pennsylvania Infantry's E Company.

Jennie had just finished hurriedly altering her brother Jack's uniform that had come in a couple of sizes too large. He was a bugler for the 21st Regiment, Pennsylvania Cavalry, and as the others set off ahead of him, Jennie had frantically altered his outfit so he could catch up with the rest of the men adequately attired. But amid the chaos of fixing the oversized uniform and worried about the oncoming battle, Jennie received some distressing news—when hearing that the Confederates were coming, residents had their hired hands take their horses out of town and toward the woods and cemetery, hiding them so as not to have them confiscated by the soldiers. Among them was Jennie's 12-year-old brother Samuel who lived in the home and worked as a delivery boy for James Pierce, a local butcher. Pierce had ordered the boy to take his family horse outside the city with the others. However, before Samuel and the other boys could get far enough away, the soldiers overtook them, placed them under arrest, and herded them back to town.

As they came into town, Margaret Pierce, the butcher's wife, noted Samuel among them. She hailed the soldiers and asked the boy to be returned safely. Jennie, too, had watched the young boys ride in and began to plead with the men and also admonished the butcher's family for endangering Samuel's life by sending him out with their horse. Then Jennie scurried to her sister's home and quietly pulled her mother aside, telling her the news. Mary Ann Wade fretfully appeared before General Early at 4:00 p.m. that day to persuade him to release her son. Much to everyone's relief, Samuel was freed and sent back to the Pierce's.

The Union army was not far behind the Confederate heels. It would be in the evening hours of June 30th before the first Union soldiers began to appear in Gettysburg, searching for Confederate soldiers after being informed they were in the town. Then, on July 1, 1863, an advance unit of the Confederate Army and an advance unit of the Union Army clashed outside Gettysburg. The Battle of Gettysburg would officially begin.

It was not long after, and as the fighting broke out, Jennie and her two younger wards fled quickly to the home of her sister, Georgia. They would join Jennie's mother at the brick Baltimore Street double-home partitioned to hold two families separately. John and Georgia McClellan owned the left side of the building, and Catherine McClain, a widow with five children, owned the right side of the building. The McClain family also remained at home during the battle.

On the morning of July 1, while Jennie Wade was finishing her chores and preparing to flee to her sister's, a division of the U.S. Army led by cavalry officer John Buford was getting attacked by rebel soldiers. Burford's division would hold the Confederates off long enough for Union reinforcements to arrive. *Image: Battles and Leaders of the Civil War*

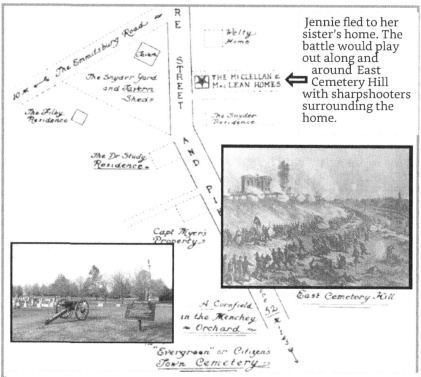

Jennie fled to her sister's home. The battle would play out along and around East Cemetery Hill with sharpshooters surrounding the home.

This map showing the location of buildings stresses the close proximity of the McClellan/McClain home to the battlefield.
Map: The true story of "Jennie" Wade, a Gettysburg maid, by J. W. Johnston.

Jennie would carry Isaac to this home belonging to her sister—Georgia (Wade) McClellan and her husband, J. Lewis McClellan and go back for 8-year-old Harry.

Georgia's home was near the cemetery; the second to the last residence along the road before heading out of town. It seemed safer there as her sister was on bed rest after giving birth—Victorian practice for women after childbirth was a "lying in" or bed rest time of two weeks to two months. Fearing for Georgia's safety at moving so close after delivery, a bed was placed in the parlor. Mother and sister remained by her side.

At this time, the battle that was raging had not made it to the house, although there was a Union picket line only feet from the back of the home. For the moment, they felt safe. But as the evening wore on, Confederate sharpshooters stationed at the tanneries down the street began to take shots at the Union sharpshooters positioned around the little brick McClellan home. The sounds of those Union soldiers who were hit, wounded, or dying in the very backyard of her sister's house and a close-by vacant lot began to permeate the walls.

It must have horrorstruck Jennie to hear those cries—she was known to be quite kind-hearted, and she had seen hard times. Her father, James Wade, had been a tailor but had been imprisoned for keeping some money he had found in the street. His imprisonment at Eastern State Penitentiary in Philadelphia had left him unable to cope. Jennie's mother, Mary Ann, petitioned the courts to have James declared insane. He was sent to the Adams County Poor House for the care he needed. To keep the family from losing their home, mother and daughter did seamstress work to pay the bills. Perhaps that was what made Jennie so empathetic toward others, including the soldiers who would come to town that summer. She knew hard times.

Jennie's childhood friend and suitor, a 21-year-old tailor (by family trade) Johnston Hastings Skelly, called Jack by his friends, had left for war. Another close friend, Wesley Culp, had relocated to Shepherdstown, Virginia as an apprentice to a carriage shop there. That childhood friend, Jack, whose mutual fondness had grown over the years, was not far away fighting for the Union Army as a corporal in the 87th Pennsylvania Volunteer Infantry. She cared deeply for him—a bond Jennie had carried through childhood. She kept his picture with her. Any one of those soldiers outside were no different than her friends, Wesley or Jack.

Jennie Wade

Wesley Culp

Jack Skelly

Three childhood friends (Jennie Wade—left, Wesley Culp-center, and Jack Skelly—right) grew up together, but their paths would change and later reconnect during the war.
Wesley: Joined the Confederate Army—He had moved away from Gettysburg, relocating with the local carriage shop he worked for to its new location in Shepherdstown, Virginia. His militia unit, the Hamtramck Guards, had been mustered into service as the Second Virginia Infantry known as the "Stonewall Brigade."
Jack: Joined the Union Army— 87th Pennsylvania Volunteer Infantry and was mustered into service on April 29, 1861.

However, Jack's mother did not approve of his relationship with Jennie. The Wade family was not wealthy and James Wade's marred reputation was the perfect fodder for wagging tongues—plenty of gossip spread about Jennie keeping company late at night while Jack was away in the army. Those hearsays also met his mother's ears, and she brought them to the attention of her son. However, when Jack sent a letter asking the young woman if the rumors were true, Jennie assured him they were not, although she did entertain innocently once in a while. Jack relayed this to his mother, scolding her for believing the lies.

Regardless, on the first day of the battle and even into the second, Jennie Wade began carrying bread and water to the Union troops. It was a seemingly endless task of pumping water from the well into a pail and then lugging it around the home and filling canteens, of baking bread and handing it out the door to soldiers needy and knocking. She dodged bullets while she did, the same hitting the home, at some points even denting the exterior. It was on July 2nd that a ten-pound shrapnel shell fired recklessly nearly two miles away from Oak Ridge smashed into the roof of the home and did not stop until it hit the brick wall on the south side of the house. It did not explode but shook the house so heartily that Jennie fainted.

The battle raged within and around the town. Image: Library of Congress

As the bread began to run out that day, Jennie and her mother planned on rising early on July 3rd to bake even as the battle raged around them. They were warned to go to their cellars to hide from the oncoming storm of bullets and cannonballs as sharpshooters might fire at any movement, and even civilians might get unintentionally picked off. Many soldiers, keen-eyed or not, had scrambled into houses and were shooting from windows at anything that moved and looked like an enemy. Many homes were occupied by Union soldiers in the front and Confederate in the rear, leaving even the smallest area a separate combat zone.

But Jennie did arise on July 3rd as the battle stormed just outside the home. A soldier came to the door early asking for bread, and Jennie told him to come back later after the baking was completed. She held bible devotions with her sister and her mother before 7:00 a.m. The explosion of bullets seemed to greaten not long after just outside the doors. The gunfire was so heavy that Jennie put down her bible and remarked: "If there is anyone in this house that is to be killed today, I hope it is me, as Georgia has that little baby." Those were the last words Georgia would hear Jennie say.

At around 8:00 a.m., Jennie began mixing the flour for bread. Some think that perhaps soldiers stationed in the Farnsworth House attic just up the street were watching for a Union soldier to come around the home again from the rear. They could see inside the windows of the house, perhaps Jennie dressed in dark clothing working the dough appeared as a soldier wearing a blue uniform. It would only be a short time later at around 8:30 a.m. when her mother joined her and Jennie kneaded the dough of the bread she was preparing that a stray Confederate musket ball would breach a wooden door on the northern side of the residence. It burst through a second door and exploded into the flesh of Jennie's back at her left shoulder blade and then sped through her heart. It only slowed as it hit her corset. Jennie Wade fell hard to the floor, her skirt barely touching her mother who was nearby. In only a breath, Jennie Wade was dead.

Hole from bullet believed to have killed Jennie.

Top : Wall and door pocked with bullet holes. And the hole made by the bullet that many believe killed Jennie Wade.

Bottom: Peering through the bullet hole and into the kitchen where Jennie was baking. The second door also has a bullet hole. The box to the left of the door is the dough box she was using to make bread for the soldiers.

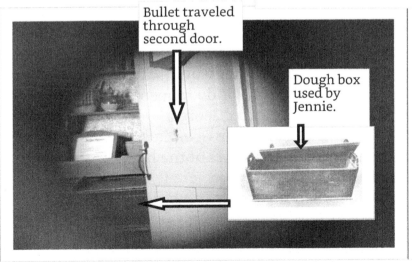

Bullet traveled through second door.

Dough box used by Jennie.

By the way—-The casket Jennie was placed in before burial was originally intended for southern General William Barksdale killed during battle, but it was left when the Confederates retreated. He was buried under a cherry tree, instead, in the yard of the Hummelbaugh Farm. And yes, Barksdale haunts that farm—

The image of Jack Skelly that Jennie had in her pocket purse the day she died.

Above: Jennie was wrapped in a quilt and placed in the cellar at rear from 8:30 a.m. on July 3rd until 1:00 p.m. July 4th while the seemingly endless battle exploded above. A vigil was kept until it was safe to bury her.

Mary Ann Wade's voice swept out softly but clearly as she felt their hoop dresses touch when her daughter collapsed. Jennie's mother would walk across the room. She would pull the parlor door open to break the news to her eldest daughter: "Georgia, your sister is dead." The screams of her sister Georgia sent Union soldiers bursting through the doors of the home. They assessed the situation and wrapped Jennie in a quilt her sister had made when she was a young child.

She was rushed to the cellar and her body placed on a wooden bench where she would lay for the next eighteen hours until the family felt it was safe enough to bury her. The remaining family crawling through a hole the soldiers made in the cellar wall between the McClellan and McClain house to gain access to the opposite, safer side of the double-home. When they felt it safe enough, Jennie's body was carefully placed in a coffin. Jennie was buried swiftly in the back yard at her sister's garden, and so quickly she still had flour and dough on her hands. Her body would be reburied twice again, once in the German Reformed Church, and then at the final resting place of Evergreen Cemetery, with a special monument erected to Jennie's memory.

But Jennie's story was not quite over. When she died, they found a small leather purse in her pocket with a key to the Breckenridge house and a picture of Jack Skelly, her love. What, you may wonder, became of Jack after she died? Several times, her two childhood friends Wesley Culp and Jack Skelly would fight on the same battlefield but opposite sides, most likely not knowing. In one—a battle near Winchester, Virginia in mid-June of 1863 with Confederate forces leaving as victors, Jack Skelly was hit by a bullet at the battle of Carter's Woods on June 16th and ultimately taken prisoner. Wesley learned that his old friend was in a Confederate hospital and gave him a visit. As he left, Jack gave him a letter to give to Jennie should his rebel friend visit Gettysburg.

Jennie's grave. Evergreen Cemetery 799 Baltimore St, Gettysburg, PA 17325 (39.819695, -77.230387)

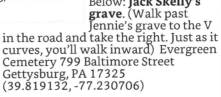

Below: **Jack Skelly's grave**. (Walk past Jennie's grave to the V in the road and take the right. Just as it curves, you'll walk inward) Evergreen Cemetery 799 Baltimore Street Gettysburg, PA 17325 (39.819132, -77.230706)

On the evening of July 1st, Confederate Wesley Culp was offered a short furlough to visit his family who were strict Union followers. He showed up at his sister's door, and she overlooked that he was a rebel soldier, thrilled to see her brother. Before Wesley left, the young man mentioned he had a message that needed delivering to Jennie's mother from Jack. His sister stated she would be more than happy to be the bearer of whatever news he had, but Wesley refused to give it to her and said he must deliver it himself.

The message would never be given. Wesley Culp died in a skirmish sometime between July 2nd and 3rd, on a farm just outside the town of Gettysburg. He was laid to rest by his comrades where he fell. Sadly, Jack Skelly also died on July 12th at the hospital in Winchester, Virginia, never knowing Jennie was killed during the Battle of Gettysburg. He was buried not far away from Jennie at Evergreen Cemetery at Gettysburg.

Even if Jennie's body is in its final resting state, Jennie is not. The brick home of Jennie's sister is now a museum called Jennie Wade House. The young woman who lost her life there still roams its walls, keeping with her good nature. She shows herself in photographs, a spirited light apparition. Some say you can catch the ghostly scent of baking bread filling the air of the kitchen. There are cold spots felt around the kitchen, sparsely decorated with an oak table, dough box, and wooden shelves filled with cookery and jars.

The Jennie Wade House Museum. You can visit it today and get a unique tour and information about Jennie's life and her death.

The Jennie Wade house today is now a museum and gift shop that offers tours of the home. It remains today as it would have appeared when Jennie and her family sought shelter within its walls. You can still see the bullet pock marks on the brick and on the door. You can take a tour and see inside of the home where Jennie was baking bread when she was shot. You can walk the steps to the cellar where Jennie's body was laid.

You may have a ghostly encounter when you visit the town—I did. The hotel behind the Jennie Wade House is the 1863 Inn of Gettysburg where we stayed during a visit. During the early morning hours, I was awakened by the sound of a bloodcurdling, high-pitched scream which continued for about thirty seconds. I lay there wide awake, then shot up from bed wondering why the rest of my family didn't awaken while I made my way to the door of the hotel. I looked outside—nothing but an occasional car passing caught my eye. I thought surely it was a dream or the scream of car brakes at the stop light just down the street. All was quiet. I went back to bed—only to be awakened five more times by this same, horrifying scream like a record repeating over and over. Could it have been the screams of Jennie's mother and sister that caught the attention of the Union soldiers who came to their aid? I don't know, but the memory is completely singed into my head and won't go away.

Sauck's Covered Bridge
Waterworks Road
Gettysburg, PA 17325
39.797338, -77.276298

Ghosts on the Way In.
Ghosts on the Way Out.

Sauck's Covered Bridge provided passage over Marsh Creek for both Union and Confederate soldiers. It is haunted by both.

Sauck's (aka Sachs) Covered Bridge was built over Marsh Creek in 1852, formed by the crisscrossing of large beams to form a lattice. It is 100 feet in length. A little over ten years after construction and during the Battle of Gettysburg, Union and Confederate troops would tread beneath its arches. On July 1, 1863, two brigades of the Union Army working their way to Gettysburg used it to cross the creek. Only four days later, Confederate troops under General Robert E Lee traversed the span as a primary line of retreat after the Union victory.

It is this rubbing of elbows with history that many believe left traces of a ghostly past at the bridge. The eerie clack of horse hooves trotting over the bridge when no horses are around have filled the air. A wisp of fog creeping within the bridge moves and wiggles, and finally shapes into the figure of a man. Cannons have been heard far-off, a phantom battle still being played out. Those who visit may be in for a start—wraithlike fingers have tugged on hair and tapped unwary shoulders. Even the scent of a cigar lingers in the air.

A couple of local legends add a terrifying twist to the reason ghosts inhabit the bridge. In one version, the hanging of three Confederate soldiers occurred here after deserting during the battle. Their shadowlike figures wander within. Another legend tells that these forms are not deserters, but the spirits of three Confederate soldiers convicted of being spies and hanged at the bridge. The two things the legends have in common, though, is that a group of Union soldiers patrolling the area found the bodies dangling by the beams. Since then, the ghosts lay claim to the historic building, lurking in the shadows and popping out to scare unwary tourists.

Servant's Old Tyme Photos
237 Steinwehr Avenue
Gettysburg, PA 17325
39.820959, -77.233610
And
Major Gen. Reynolds Monument
Herbst Woods
55 Reynolds Avenue S
Gettysburg, PA 17325
39.834405, -77.250959

Secret Affairs

General John Reynolds was killed at the start of the battle of Gettysburg in a wooded area. But his ghost shows up somewhere else as did his secret. *Artist Alfred Waud. Library of Congress*

General John F. Reynolds, age 42, was a United States Military Academy West Point graduate and a career military man. He was also a respected Union general. He fought in a number of battles before the Civil War but found himself just a couple hours into the Battle of Gettysburg on July 1st directing positions in the heart of the combat.

Above: The place where General John Reynolds was killed. The man on the left is pointing to the general area. There is a monument there marking the place he was mortally wounded today:
Major Gen. Reynolds monument
55 Reynolds Ave S, Gettysburg, PA 17325
(39.834411, -77.250958)
Image: Library of Congress
Left: An image showing an old marker for the location.

As he was supervising on horseback the placement of soldiers, he cried out, "Forward men! For God's sake, forward!" He turned slightly in the saddle to look toward a ridge, stood upon his stirrups, and waved his sword above his men's heads. It was between 10:15 and 10:30 a.m. Just moments after the words swept from his lips, Reynolds tumbled from his horse. A Minié ball (a small torpedo-shaped, grooved bullet) was sent from the muzzle loading gun of a marksman shooting from a tree and struck Reynolds in the back of the neck.

His orderly, a Sergeant Veil, went swiftly to his side after he saw the man fall from his horse and knelt next to him. He realized Reynolds had died instantly. Upon loosening Reynold's military shirt collar, he revealed a small silver chain with a Roman Catholic medal and a gold ring in the form of clasped hands dangling beneath it. "Dear Kate" was inscribed within the gold ring. But the war was raging around them, and there was little time to note such an ornament. His lifeless body was hastily wrapped in a blanket and was carried swiftly by aides to the home of George George as not to shake the morale of his soldiers during the fight.

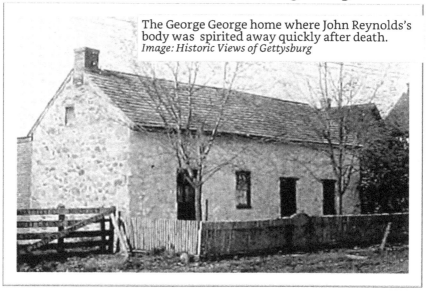

The George George home where John Reynolds's body was spirited away quickly after death.
Image: Historic Views of Gettysburg

His remains and personal belongings were sent to the home of his sister Catherine on Spruce Street in Philadelphia, including some letters found signed by someone named Kate. And he should have been laid to rest. Yet, he and his secret were not dead. If you expect the ghost of John F. Reynolds to show up as a hell-bent soldier on the battleground, sword waving in the air, and a battle cry ringing out, you may be as shocked as his family when they found out he was not the married -to-the military, bachelor type they thought he was. The general who may have appeared on the exterior as a career-focused man also had a shroud of secrecy lingering around him, along with a soft place in his heart for a mysterious woman. And his ghost, it shows up not on the battlefield, but in an area not far away.

Upon receiving his personal effects, it came as a surprise to his family that his West Point military class ring was missing. And there was a little necklace and a gold ring with a woman's name inscribed within. Who was this mysterious Kate? The family would soon find out when a grief-stricken young woman showed up two days before the funeral and asked politely if "Miss Hewitt" could view the remains. Eleanor Reynolds, his sister, came to the door and inquired: "Is it—Kate?"

It was the mysterious Kate, and the family embraced the young woman with open arms, even writing later that they surely regretted John Reynolds

The mysterious woman in General John Reynolds's life —the beautiful Kate Hewitt for whom he was so smitten.

had never told them about her, and the family had never met the young woman. She shared the long vigil overnight with his sister before the funeral. Her name was Kate Hewitt, and not once among the letters he had sent to his close-knit family had he mentioned her in his writing. As far as they knew, their brother and son was a confirmed bachelor with no plans to marry.

But he had plans. Raised as a protestant, he had met the 26-year-old governess (Catherine "Kate" Mary Hewitt) in 1860. Both were on a ship—he was heading to West Point to take a position as commandant. Kate was working at the Catholic girls' school run by the Daughters of Charity and heading to Philadelphia with plans of converting to the Catholic faith. Despite their differences in age and background, the two fell deeply in love and planned to marry— secretly, that is. And then, the war came.

They both knew what could transpire as John headed off to war. The two arranged that should John die, Kate would continue her aspirations and serve as a Daughter of Charity. Perhaps. Still, it must have been a shock when she heard the news John had died in battle. She did as she promised, joining the faith at Mother Seton Convent in Emmitsburg, Maryland. In 1868, she returned home most likely due to her very ill health but never married.

Kate lived in Stillwater, New York until she died of pneumonia in 1902. The word 'Mizpah' is carved on her gravestone, a Hebrew blessing meaning, 'May God watch over you until we are together again.' Her ghost is still around, though—a young woman walking the battlefield, searching for her lost love, John.

Herbst Woods/monument where General Reynolds was killed and his secret betrothed still wanders looking for him.

Major Gen. Reynolds monument—55 Reynolds Avenue S, Gettysburg, PA 17325 (39.834389, -77.250959)

The George George home where Reynolds was taken after death. Perhaps the two have found each other in eternity. Now, Servant's Old Tyme Photos— 237 Steinwehr Avenue Gettysburg, PA 17325 (39.820906, -77.233625)

Maybe they have both found each other. Another story tells that a man has been seen in the old George George Home lying on a cot where John Reynolds's body was taken after his death. Above the man, a mysterious woman in black hovers with a candle. The old home is now Servants Old Tyme Photos, where you can get your portrait taken in period clothing—and perhaps catch a glimpse of a ghost!

This photo "Field Where General Reynolds Fell" by photographer O'Sullivan, Timothy H., 1840-1882 shows the many men who died that day. It is not surprising with so many deaths in the area of Herbst woods and all the battlefields are haunted. *Image: LOC*

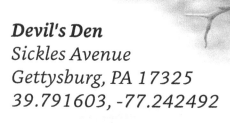

Devil's Den
Sickles Avenue
Gettysburg, PA 17325
39.791603, -77.242492

Dying in Devil's Den and Coming Back Again

Where people frolic today, was the last place many men saw alive on the day of a momentous battle at Devil's Den just below Little Round Top.

If you didn't know the history, you would think they are just scattered boulders and raggedy trees lying below a hill now called Little Round Top. Between that hill and these boulders is a stream called Plum Run that leaves a lot of soggy, marshy spots. But there is history. And there are ghosts.

On the second day of the Battle of Gettysburg, July 2nd, 1863, fighting at this rock outcrop was intense, bloody, and violent. Almost 8,000 men would battle as General Lee's Confederate troops attacked Major Sickle's Corps of the Army of the Potomac. It was a victorious battle for the South amidst many defeats on their side that day as the Union troops retreated. It was a loss for the many men who would die for that battle; many picked off by Confederate sharpshooters who moved into the safety of the rocks and clefts of Devil's Den, firing at the Union soldiers and officers atop Little Round Top. There were dead, lots of dead.

A dead sharpshooter in Devil's Den.

They come back, those dead. Visitors come home with ghostly images of a mysterious headless rider on horseback. They also see ghostly apparitions quite often, and camera batteries are known to die around the site, returning to normal after tourists have gotten into their car and pulled away. Johlene Riley, a local author, gives a possible explanation for this occurrence in one of her books, *Ghost Encounters of Gettysburg*. She tells that war photographers would come in after the battles and stage the soldiers' bodies and their weapons, moving them to different locations to make them more dramatic or suitable for a story. Perhaps this discourtesy to the corpse was not appreciated by the dead, and they return the disrespect by eking out the energy within camera batteries—and the reason some folks have found blurry images of soldiers.

A staged photograph at Devil's Den. Unlike many dead soldiers moved to get a more appealing shots and to capture the war's toll on death right after the battle, these men were actually alive and well! *Library of Congress*

Mark Nesbitt, historian and leading authority on Gettysburg and its many ghosts, worked as a park ranger in the Gettysburg National Military Park. He has chronicled hundreds of stories of the paranormal in the area—one he relates is of a young woman who was climbing the huge boulders dotting the landscape at Devil's Den. She felt something snatch at her ankle. Shocked, she looked down into the dark crevice beneath her. Staring back at her was a man wearing a Civil War uniform. When she screamed, he vanished!

Devil's Den.

View looking down from Little Round Top

Devil's Den

Plum Run

Plum Run

If you stand on the top of Little Round Top and look to the valley toward Devil's Den, you'll be staring at *The Valley of Death*—the nickname given for the Plum Run basin (arrows), a creek between Devil's Den and Little Round Top that was said to run with blood during the battle. It is also a hotbed for ghostly sounds and sights from twinkling lights to the bangs of cannon and guns. Some even catch the phantom scent of gun smoke.

But the most well-known ghost story coming from Devil's Den is that of the barefoot Texan soldier with tousled long-haired and outfitted in a flimsy government-issue butternut shirt. He's quite unkempt and donning a floppy slouch hat with a dented crown

and the front flipped up. When he walks up to visitors, he points at Plum Run and greets hikers with: *What you're looking for is over there.* Then he disappears.

A Confederate soldier in a slouch hat and jacket. Image: Library of Congress

If you're curious of the location of Plum Run—if you pull into the parking lot at Devil's Den headfirst with your rear to Devil's Den, it is the teeny creek about 70 feet away.

Some men of the 1st Texas. If you take a trip to Gettysburg and visit Devil's Den, you just might run into one of them— *Image: The Photographic History of The Civil War in Ten Volumes, 1911*

But why would the spirit of a Texan soldier show up there? The 1st Texas Infantry Regiment got their nickname the "Ragged Old First" from the scruffy clothing they wore and the bold stance they took in battle. When they first left Texas, they were so poorly armed and uniformed, many brought their own guns from home, and some didn't have any at all.

During the fight at Devil's Den, the 1st Texas Infantry Regiment, under the command of Major General John Bell Hood and incredibly outnumbered, pushed forward and drove the Union's artillery guns and the soldiers out of the boulder-ridden chunk of land. Quickly, 1st Texas sent in sharpshooters who began to take out Yankee officers on Little Roundtop. There were 1,800 Rebel casualties during this fight, and one of them in his butternut shirt and floppy slouch has returned to greet visitors at the park.

Little Round Top
Sykes Avenue
Gettysburg, PA 17325
39.791950, -77.237042

Ghostly War Heroes of Little Round Top

Little Round Top, Gettysburg, July 2, 1863. The Union holding off the Confederates ended in an epic charge. And ghosts.
Harper's Weekly Magazine, July 25, 1863

On the morning of July 2nd and in the heat of the Battle of Gettysburg, only a few Union soldiers stood atop a nearly barren but boulder-ridden hilltop south of Gettysburg, the extreme left flank of Union lines. The larger forces were laid out just a bit to the north. However, this little piece of higher ground nearly overlooked by Union commanders would, within the next July-sweltering 24 hours, become a significant turning point for the war as just a handful of Union soldiers fought against repeated assaults from much larger troops of Confederate soldiers.

If the Confederates had seized Little Round Top that day, they might have invaded the left flank of the entire Union Army, and perhaps won the battle. Instead, Union soldiers feverishly rushed to the location. The men immediately opened fire, and the intense and bloody fighting at Little Round Top began with Confederates charging the hill and their sharpshooters, protected by the rocks at Devil's Den just beyond, returning fire. The 20th Maine Regiment, nearly out of ammunition after holding off the enemy for almost an hour and a half, made a daring charge down the hill to defend Little Round Top. On that day, 134 of the 2,996 Union soldiers would die from their wounds. More than 279 of the 4,864 Confederates lay dead. Many of these were by bayonet point as the Union soldiers began to run out of ammunition.

Confederate soldiers laying at the "slaughter pit" below Little Round top where so many were killed for their cause. *Image: Library of Congress*

Visitors taking in the area have reported hearing gunshots, cries of battle, and the sound of drums. During the filming of a Civil War movie Gettysburg in 1993, several extras on the set were taking a break on Little Round Top. After hearing the rustling of leaves behind them, they looked up to see a scruffy older man in a raggedy private's Union uniform. He reeked of the sulfur odor that surrounds the black powder used in old muskets. A stubbled beard covered his chin and cheeks. He made it quite clear he was angry that a battle was taking place. "Rough day, boys?" he asked them. He then held out his hand and gave the actors some spare rounds of ammunition before he left along the trail, disappearing. The strange encounter unsettled the group enough that they had the musket rounds checked. Sure enough, they were genuine and not the fake prop ammo used for the set!

Little Round Top, then. Just remember that not everyone has the passion for ghost watching when they visit these areas. Always be discreet when looking for ghosts on these hallowed grounds. *Image: Library of Congress*

Little Round Top now. You can walk a trail at Little Round Top and stand where so many soldiers fought for their lives. There is a tower overlook to get a full view of the battlefield. People taking ghostly pictures here often have their camera batteries die, only to revive when they leave.

Watch for a bristle-faced man dressed in soldier attire grumbling about the war. He may be a ghostly visitor!

Walking where a battle was fought. A rampart at Little Round Top. Beyond—is Big Round Top.

Looking down from Little Round Top to Devil's Den where Confederate sharpshooters picked off Union soldiers.

The Road to Little Round Top
Sykes Avenue
Gettysburg, PA 17325
39.791950, -77.237042

Rumors of the Ghost of Washington

Did this man's troops hear tales of a famous ghost while climbing this hill ? Joshua Chamberlain heard the rumors, but were they true? Photo: *Pickerill, Elmo N. , Collector. Little Round Top.* LOC

Little Round Top.

There is a story of early dignitaries visiting Little Round Top after the battle. They were honored that a group of reenactors had set up a scene of the battle at Devil's Den below specifically for them, only to find out there were none set up at all!

Joshua Lawrence Chamberlain attended both Bowdoin College and Bangor Theological Seminary but chose to be a professor at Bowdoin College teaching languages and rhetoric instead of becoming a minister. With no background in the military, but desperately desiring to serve his country, Chamberlain volunteered for service in the Union Army in 1862.

On July 2nd, he was leading the beat-up, undermanned 20th Maine, known to be a bit rag-tag and unruly, on Little Round Top and the far left flank and awaiting another Confederate attack. They had maintained their stand as best they could to this point but were running out of ammunition. Chamberlain's men were becoming fewer and fewer.

At any point, Chamberlain knew if his men retreated, the Confederates would march right into the rear of the Union Army. But his men were at breaking point. Then after another attempt by the Confederates, Chamberlain was able to rouse his soldiers into making a desperate bayonet charge down the hillside, surprising the rebel soldiers into retreating.

But what had possibly given those worn soldiers renewed faith and vigor? Before the battle and along the way to Gettysburg on a forced 16-mile march, Chamberlain would describe some strange rumors that filtered through the ranks as they headed to Little Round Top. Nerves were on edge as the darkness of night had enveloped the soldiers. They were hungry, aching, and dirt-tired. They knew at the end of this God -forsaken march just like every God-forsaken march before it, there would be a battle, and the odds were high they would die.

They had already heard the morale-breaking news that the Confederate Army had driven back the Union, and among those dead was John Reynolds. Few men were holding on to the last shreds of the Union, and if troops didn't get there by morning, it was all over. Then, a staff officer had ridden his horse along with the marching men, telling officers that McClellan (who was well-liked by his men but had been removed from command for not pursuing the Confederate Army after Antietam) was back in power. He had not been reinstated even though a great roar of approval came from the men. Not long after, the whispers began to flow that the ghostly form of George Washington was riding along the hills of Gettysburg at sunset. He had parted clouds to allow his presence to be seen and had shown troops that stopped at a forked section of road unsure which way to travel the right direction to get them on their way.

"Let no one smile at me!" Chamberlain had been quoted in Hearst Magazine in an interview later, "I half believed it myself,—so did the powers of the other world draw nigh!" Chamberlain was a professor of rhetoric, teaching speakers/writers the art of both persuasion and motivation in communicating to particular audiences and situations. Did he use those tools in convincing his troops of Washington's intervention to maintain their stand that night?

Whether a ghost had displayed itself to the Union Army or not, perhaps those fighting the battle were bolstered by the thought such a great commander had come back from the grave to support their cause. When asked many, many years later, if the rumors of the ghost were true, he answered—"Yes, that report was circulated through our lines, and I have no doubt that it had a tremendous psychological effect in inspiring the men. Doubtless, it was a superstition, but who among us can say that such a thing was impossible. We know not what mystic power may be possessed by those who are now bivouacking with the dead. I only know the effect, but I dare not explain or deny the cause. Who shall say that Washington was not among the number of those who aided the country that he founded?"

Dobbin House Tavern
89 Steinwehr Avenue
Gettysburg, PA 17325
39.822756, -77.232662

Home. Field Hospital. Tavern. Haunt.

Reverend Alexander Dobbin, minister of Rock Creek Presbyterian Church located just a mile north of present-day Gettysburg, built the Dobbin House. The building is over 200 years old, and once used as a home and college academy. Reverend Dobbin was said to be short, stout, and quite happy. He had ten children with his first wife, who passed away. He inherited nine more children when he married his second wife. The Dobbin House has ties to the underground railroad (runaway slaves were harbored in a secret crawlspace in the home) and also to the Civil War as a field hospital. Now it is a restaurant, inn, and a place where ghosts show up. Those dining at the restaurant have seen ghostly soldiers, nurses, and even the minister himself. A little girl ghost peers out windows!

The Jacob Hummelbaugh Farm
Pleasonton Avenue
Gettysburg, PA 17325
39.807943, -77.231564

The Baying Phantom Hound of Hummelbaugh Farm

Hummelbaugh Farm. *Photo: Brenda Neuroth-AllVisionsArt*

William Barksdale. *Library of Congress*

Southern Democrat William Barksdale was a staunch advocate of state's rights and pro-slavery, and he wasn't quiet about his views while a congressman. But on February 5th, 1858, and before the start of the

Civil War, during a fight on the House floor between pro-slavery and anti-slavery legislators, Barksdale unintentionally helped break up one of the most infamous brawls in the legislative history. During the fight, one of his adversaries, Cadwallader Washburn, reached out to grab Barksdale by the hair to punch him in the face—but Barksdale ducked. Instead, the man ended up with nothing but the wig donning Barksdale's head clutched in his fist. Washburn quickly handed the wig back. However, in his embarrassment, Barksdale unwittingly stuck the wig on backward. A witness remarked later that the incident was so comical, everyone stopped bickering to laugh!

Later, as a Confederate officer Barksdale and his troops, known as the Barksdale's Mississippi Brigade, seemed unstoppable. Barksdale fought hard in the battles of Bull Run, Harpers Ferry, and Antietam. After, he headed on to engage in combat at Gettysburg. He was mortally wounded on July 2nd while leading a brutal attack at Cemetery Ridge, smashing through the Union troops. But to bring him down, it took a gunshot to his left knee, a cannonball hitting his left foot, and lastly, a bullet to his chest that knocked him from his mount. As he lay upon the ground, he called out to his aide and yelled: "I am killed! Tell my wife and children that I died fighting at my post!"

He was found by Union soldiers and taken to the Jacob Hummelbaugh farmhouse, a field hospital. Robert Cassiday, a musician from the 148th Pennsylvania, was stationed at the hospital and attended to the man offering him water until he could receive a good dose of morphine. Barksdale died the next day from his wounds. He was buried in a temporary grave behind the Hummelbaugh house.

They say you can still hear the general calling for water when near the old white building, now owned by the National Park Service. But even more ominous is that you may also hear the baying howl of his old hunting dog on the farm. When Barksdale's wife, Narcissa, made her way to Gettysburg to exhume her husband's remains and return them to Jackson, Mississippi in 1867, she brought with her the general's favorite hunting dog. The hound went immediately to the general's grave at the Hummelbaugh farmhouse, and even after Barksdale's body was exhumed and placed in the wagon for the long journey to Mississippi, the dog refused to leave. Distraught, his wife tried over and over to persuade him to go with her. Instead, he whined and howled and carried on, and nothing could convince him to leave that place.

Although those living near the Hummelbaugh farm tried to coax the dog away with food and shelter after Barksdale's wife left, it would never desert its post, and eventually, the old hound died where his owner's body was temporarily laid to rest. But on certain nights, you can hear the heart-wrenching howl of that dog, mourning for his old master. And you might see his shadow lurking around the backyard of the house.

The Jacob Hummelbaugh Farm Pleasonton Avenue, Gettysburg, PA 17325 (39.807917, -77.231550)
Photo: Brenda Neuroth-AllVisionsArt

The Charge of Elon Farnsworth
S Confederate Avenue
Gettysburg, PA 17325
39.786910, -77.243800

Pale Rider on a Ghostly Steed

Above: Farnsworth's suicidal charge. *From: Johnson, Robert Underwood, and Buel, Clarence C. (eds.), Battles and Leaders of the Civil War, Vol. 3*
Right: General Elon John Farnsworth of Co. K, 8th Illinois Cavalry Regiment. *Library of Congress*

Brigadier General Elon J. Farnsworth was known for more than a few daring mischiefs and hijinks during his college years; plucky Farnsworth was expelled along with eight others when during a drinking spree with classmates, one student died falling off a house. Upon leaving the college, Farnsworth went to the professor of history, Dr. Andrew White, and acknowledged he had done wrong and hoped he could show that he could make a man of himself one day. He had decided to join the military. The fearless (but perhaps a bit reckless) leader of a group of college students who had made a brash decision in youth was true to his word as a man.

Five years later, on June 28, 1863, after showing courage on the battlefield, Elon Farnsworth was promoted from a mere captain to brigadier general. He would lead a charge driving the Confederates out of Hanover, Pennsylvania, 24 miles from Gettysburg. Then, less than a week later, in the late afternoon of July 3rd in Gettysburg, Union Brigadier General Hugh Judson Kilpatrick ordered him to make a suicidal charge against the Confederate lines through thick woods and huge boulders, a seemingly impossible task.

The area of Little Round Top (left) and Big Round Top (right) showing the rocky terrain the foot soldiers and the calvary would have to traverse. *Photo: NPS.org*

It was not far from the Slyder Farm by Plum Run and near Big Round Top where Farnsworth protested vehemently, telling the general that the charge would be futile and unwise through rough, boulder-strewn ground thick with fallen trees. However, Kilpatrick accused Farnsworth of cowardice. The daring boy who would become a fearless man did as ordered, personally leading his brigade on an ill-fated charge. Farnsworth was shot down along with 65 of his men by the 15th Alabama Infantry. He was only 25-years-old. He was found on July 5th where he had fallen just beyond a row of fencing, his body riddled with five bullets.

Monument to the 1st Vermont Volunteer Cavalry Regiment at Gettysburg near the spot where Farnsworth lost his life. *Photo: Alexey Mukhranov*

Some who walk the area beneath Big Round Top and along the path of Farnsworth's suicidal charge have felt hard belly pangs and a sense of massive doubt. Working upward along the Big Round Top trail seems to give the opposite impression—an elated feeling of euphoria. The area is off the beaten path of Little Round Top, so the roar of crowds doesn't always drown out the ghostly whispers of the past. The cries of battle—screams of human anguish and shrieks of dying horses echo in the area. A ghostly pale figure was spotted in the mid-1900s riding near the route that the ill-fated charge took place—perhaps it is Elon Farnsworth still riding long after death.

Farnsworth House
and
Sweney's Tavern
401 Baltimore Street
Gettysburg, PA 17325
39.825533, -77.231288

The Very Spirited Farnsworth House

Farnsworth House - The battle would play out in the streets and even in the home with sharpshooters strategically placed in the attic to shoot toward the fighting on Cemetery Hill. Now, it is haunted by both ghosts from the battle and others who have somehow been touched by the home.

There's a house named after Elon Farnsworth within the town of Gettysburg proper—The Farnsworth House. It is quite haunted. Tanner John F. McFarlane built the home—portions date back to 1810, followed by the brick structure added in 1833. The building has changed hands a few times over the years, including ownership by Harvey Sweney, who was a

Gettysburg teacher and later a butcher. He purchased the house on April 7, 1852. He lived in the home off and on with his wife, Catherine, and children into the 1860s. It came to a more recent stop with the Loren Shultz family, who purchased the property in 1972 and made it an inn and restaurant. That's when it received its Farnsworth name.

During the Battle of Gettysburg, the fighting did not occur just outside the city proper where some locals perceived it would take place. As it transpired, the combat also emerged in the streets of the town and even within the homes and businesses. Townspeople who were unable to flee at this time unsafely huddled in their cellars by day as the fighting ensued and, if lucky, worked their way upstairs at night when the battle decreased. The Harvey Sweney family, owners of the house at the time, were one of those families. The scars from hundreds of bullets left over from the 3-day Battle of Gettysburg still pockmarking the brick walls lay testimony to the fortress it provided for them.

The upper, tiny attic window where Confederate sharpshooters were posted to shoot Union soldiers. Their ghosts can still be heard. *Photo courtesy Farnsworth House Inn.*

The Haunted Attic

At some point during combat, the Farnsworth House became a post for Confederate sharpshooters who stationed themselves in the attic window facing the street due to its vantage point for firing on troops fighting at Cemetery Hill. Once there, the soldiers dragged heavy trunks and chests across the close-quartered room and beneath the windows to gain easy access and to obtain the best position.

Playing a mouth harp.

The attic where a phantom sniper still guards his post and plays soft tunes on his mouth harp. *Photo courtesy Farnsworth House Inn.*

When not firing at Union soldiers from their perches at the windows, the snipers wiled away their time chattering softly and playing music on their mouth harps, a small instrument that makes a boing-boing sounding tune. Now, visitors can hear the soft, eerie twang of music seeping from the attic, ghostly footsteps walking, and the grind of objects dragged across the floor, perhaps a wooden box drawn across the surface to sit upon or attain access to the windows.

Apparitions in the Dining Area/Tavern

You can grab a sumptuous bite to eat before taking a ghost tour here. Or have lunch and a beer after staying the night. And watch for ghosts when you do!

The tavern is a popular hangout for Civil War re-enactors—both Union and Confederate who drop old grudges to share a beer with each other and once in a while, with a ghost.

If you are a patron of the dining room and tavern, you might run into a female spirit who wanders around the kitchen and dining area tables, once in a while tugging on the apron strings of servers. She appears quite lifelike dressed in period clothing while she straightens shelves once lining the walls, but no longer there. She has even appeared in a hazy hue, reaching out to break the fall of a worker wearing a historical costume. Perhaps the spirit believed she was one of the other ghosts that call the Farnsworth House home. A certain Lady in White with piercing blue eyes peers out the tavern window too.

The Stairway

The apparition of an elderly lady with gray hair primly pulled back at the nape of the neck and donning a dark, old fashioned dress with an apron tied at the waist likes to putter around the inn. The scent of roses follows in her wake. She strolls the stairway and roams the hallways upstairs. And this ghostly lady will occasionally check on the guests of the Sleepy Hollow Ghost Tours presented at the Farnsworth House, startling those who attend because at first, they think she is a part of the presentation. They call her Mary and believe she was visiting her brother in Gettysburg during the battle, but on her trip ended up tending to wounded soldiers brought to the home. Although she didn't die during the fighting, she must have found her calling so long ago because she will check on guests that might be feeling a little under the weather.

The stairway and halls where Mary quietly walks.

The cellar appears to be a favorite place for many ghosts—good or bad.

Cellar

During the three day battle, soldiers were wounded in the streets, many laying there until they died. One made his way to the Farnsworth House Inn (at the time, the Harvey Sweney home) and crawled for safety from the sharpshooters down the steps to the cellar door where he died. When Catherine Sweney and her 20-year-old daughter, Elizabeth, returned, they found his body in a pool of blood. The poor soldier was buried, but his spirit remains in the cellar—chairs move, and a few lucky women have even felt soft whiskers rub their cheeks. And apparitions are showing up in cameras, dark-shadow figures with top hats and canes, ghostly relics of the past. There is also a particular ghost who likes the dank and dark cellar but does not like women. He might send a glass cup flying or tug a little too hard on a shirt. The basement is now part of the Farnsworth ghost tours and ghost hunts and decorated to look like a Victorian mourning parlor. There's a mirror in the front of the room. Take a picture of yourself in it, and you might find a ghostly friend with you in the image.

A Couple Haunted Rooms

The Catherine Sweney Room gets its name from the owner of the inn during the Gettysburg battle. Many claim this is one of the most haunted rooms. A midwife mourning over the death of a stillborn visits this room

The cozy and beautiful Catherine Sweney Room has a caring ghostly presence. *Photo courtesy Farnsworth House Inn.*

and sometimes sits on the side of the bed as if gently watching over whoever is lying there. She can leave a sense of sadness in her wake that dissipates as quickly as it came. The midwife paces outside the room, but when lodgers open the door to peer out and follow the sound of footsteps, no one is there!

The Sara Black Room is in the central portion of the house overlooking Baltimore Street. There is a canopy bed along with an antique marble-top dresser, and a bathroom with a claw foot tub/shower. It was once the main bedroom of the home, and the bathroom was a nursery.

Sara Black Room. Photo courtesy Farnsworth House Inn.

Sara Black Room bathroom. *Photo courtesy Farnsworth House Inn.*

One of the most active and playful little spirits resides in this room. Blankets are tugged by a 5-year-old who was run over by a carriage in the streets below. The child was carried upstairs to this room but passed away. Fondly called Jeremy by the innkeepers, he loves to run up and down the hallways and will tug on the hair of women. Things move in this room quite often. One guest had a child's wooden-wheeled toy duck slide across the floor and beneath the bed in the middle of the night.

The Inn offers walks, tours, and stays for the history -lover and the ghost-lover. There is a restaurant for dining and a tavern. I ate at the tavern, and the food was delicious and historical. But the best way to experience these spirits, of the spooky kind or the drink, is to visit here yourself!

My own ghostly image from the Farnsworth—a little boy peering out an upper room window— none other than the Sara Black Room! Perhaps it is the little boy hit by the carriage—Jeremy.

National Homestead
Orphanage & Widow's Home
777 Baltimore Street
Gettysburg, PA 17325
39.822455, -77.230772

The Dead Soldier & The Orphanage

A soldier lay dead after the Brickyard Fight during the Battle of Gettysburg. In his hands, he clasped a picture of three small children. Who was this soldier?

In the 1860s, John Kuhn's brickyard was on 221 North Stratton Street. There were just a few homes there, including his own built in 1860. Mister Kuhn, along with his wife, five children, and two teenaged boys (probably hired hands), lived a typically quiet life at home. During that time, the property was still considered rural and outside Gettysburg proper.

It was surrounded mostly by wheat fields, occasional farmhouses, and fences. But on the early morning hours of July 1st, 1863, the Civil War would bring their serene, rustic life to an abrupt halt. And before the day would end, the ravages of war would not only change the countryside at John Kuhn's brickyard forever, it would also alter the lives of the doomed 27th Pennsylvania, 154th New York infantry, and the 134th New York Infantry by the sacrifice of this Union brigade to buy time for another.

It was Kuhn's fence row where the Brickyard Fight would begin and end on that overcast and humid 80-degree day. It had been raining off and on and quite dismal, except when occasionally the off-blue sky would peek through. It was right there that Union troops were losing ground. The right flank was quickly collapsing to the Confederates. Reinforcements were called in, and Union Colonel Charles Coster, a mere 23-years-old and already set up at Cemetery Hill would arrive as support around mid-afternoon. His men were no more than a few regiments of mostly New Yorkers and Pennsylvanians, a trifling number compared to what was in force as the battle raged at Cemetery Hill.

For the time, the men found shelter behind the post and rail fence along the Kuhn property and in front of the kilns. And they held the Confederates at bay, at least long enough that the Union soldiers could advance and the grounds of Cemetery Hill could be secured. But at a cost. As many as 500 of Coster's brigade were casualties of war, scattered around the streets where they were killed instantly or had crawled to get respite from gunfire.

It was overcast with intermittent rain when a girl found the corpse of one of those Union soldiers several days later. He was hidden partly in an overgrown fenced lot adjacent to the clapboard home of Judge

Samuel Russell, located on the corner of Stratton and York. The body of the unknown man was just short of a quarter-mile from the brickyard. Most likely, he dumped his gear in a desperate attempt to escape the onslaught of Confederates pouring into the town because he had nothing to identify him. Except, that is, and upon closer inspection, an ambrotype photograph of three young children which he clutched tightly in his dead fingers.

Where an unidentified body of a soldier was found lying in a secluded area at York and Stratton streets holding an ambrotype of three little children in his fingers. *Image: John Richter Collection*

She was the curious daughter of Benjamin Shriver who found the image. Benjamin was a former resident of the town who was at the time of the battle living 13 miles west of Gettysburg and working both as a postmaster and as proprietor of Graefenburg Springs tavern. Along with many, including curiosity seekers and souvenir hunters throughout the countryside, the family had probably come into Gettysburg after the battle to check on relatives still living there and to see the outcome of the fighting. From her hands, the picture went to her father, who displayed the memento of war in his tavern for all to see.

Had it not been for the breakdown of a wagon along the roadway running from Chambersburg to Gettysburg, the unidentified soldier and the three children may not have been found. The picture might have sat above the pub hearth, nothing but a curio swiped from a dead man's hands and something to start a conversation about the war on cold winter nights. But while rushing to the battlefield to provide volunteer aid to the wounded, the carriage of 49-year-old physician John Francis Bourns and several other doctors had to be repaired, and the closest town just happened to be Graefenburg. The twist of fate left them taking respite at Benjamin Shriver's tavern, where they learned the tale of how the picture ended up in the bar. Intrigued, Doctor Bourns convinced Benjamin Shriver to give him the image so he could find the identity of the children, and such, the name of the man who clasped their picture in his dying hands.

This *carte de visite* was created by Doctor Bourns to find the children.

Doctor Bourns copied the picture and sent the story to newspapers. He also sold copies of the photograph mounted on a piece of card called carte de visite, which were quite popular as collectibles at the time. The dead soldier was recognized when his wife, Philinda, saw a plea in a local paper to identify the children. She wrote to Doctor Bourns from her Portville, New York home and stated she had sent such a picture to her husband but had not heard from him since the Battle of Gettysburg. He was 30-year-old, Sergeant Amos Humiston, a harness maker by trade. But he was also from Company C, 154th New York Volunteers who had battled at the brickyard.

Coster Avenue and monuments to the soldiers who fought there and where the Brickyard Fight would leave a heavy toll on soldiers like Amos Humiston. A mural now dons a wall depicting the battle. NPS—Battle Trail. 154th New York Volunteer Infantry Monument Gettysburg, PA 17325 (39.835130, -77.227574)

The marker where Amos Humiston's body was found with the picture of his children.

101 N Stratton St Gettysburg, PA 17325 (39.832036, -77.228710)

There is a beautiful mural portraying the battle painted on the side of a building where the brickyard once stood. Some will testify that the land of the old brickyard and the area where Humiston's body was discovered is haunted. No surprise with all the soldiers who died there. Could the ghost of Amos Humiston still be hanging around? Perhaps. When you visit, take a moment and ask!

A view of the orphanage in better times—or staged to appear so. *Image: Library of Congress.*

The National Homestead of Gettysburg was developed in 1866 to create an orphanage for children and a home for widows of soldiers who had died due to the Civil War. It was located at the foot of Cemetery Hill. It was created in part by funds collected from Doctor Bourns' sales of the carte de visite of Amos and Philinda Humiston's children. It was officially opened with 22 children—12 boys and ten girls—within its care in November 1866. Though, within a few years and in its heyday the institution became overcrowded with as many as 124 children. A newer building was added to house the overflow of children. Missus Humiston would become part of the initial staff with her children Frank, Frederick, and Alice, by her side.

The state did not pay for the orphanage. Public contributions were taken instead, and by 1870, funding and donations began to dwindle. Advertisements placed in newspapers asked for communities to donate food for the children, and most came from the town of Gettysburg. There were good times then, still. Rewards were given to good little children like sleigh rides and attending town events such as strewing flowers on the graves of soldiers each year.

It was during this time that the initial headmistress was replaced by Rosa J. Carmichael in 1872, who dealt out punishments cruelly. She took away the rewards, including the scattering of flowers and, instead, made the children watch the town children do so behind a fence. She was known to shackle children over rain barrels in a dank, windowless pit in the cellar as a discipline. She locked one 4-year-old child in the outhouse on a freezing December night who was, by luck, found by two local men returning home from work who heard his cries.

Shackles used on children.

The pit where naughty children were punished. And maybe some who were not so bad. Although records are sparse, it is believed that some children may not have left this cellar alive.

A view of the orphanage—then.
Library of Congress.

And a view now.

The Waynesboro Village Record reported that a 16-year-old boy dressed in rags and barefoot had made his way into the town. He stated he had escaped the orphanage and that Rosa Carmichael had forced his sisters, both17-years-old, the scandalous punishment of wearing boys' clothing.

On June 11, 1876, local authorities arrested Carmichael charging cruelty to the children and the orphanage in part due to information disclosed by an orphan George W. Lundon. It closed its doors in shame at her actions. According to historians, the Skelly Post of the Grand Army of the Republic gave her 24 hours to get out of town after she paid her $20.00 fine (reduced because of her gender) and the court costs due to assault and battery of the children.

You can tour the orphanage now. I did. My family took the Orphanage Ghost Tour with Gettysburg Battlefield Tours with our tour guide Jim. We weren't twenty minutes into our hotel room in Gettysburg, Pennsylvania, before we had to drop our suitcases unopened on the bed and rush down for the ghost tour across the street. Like so many who travel from faraway places to this little section of Pennsylvania, we came to get a taste of the ghostly fare. As we pushed open the front doors and crossed the threshold from the well-lit foyer of the bright and modern 1863 Inn of Gettysburg and out into shadowy streets, there was a certain unsettling aura in the darkness enveloping us. No worries—surely, there would be a long walk by a tour guide to a lonesome street with a few light ghost stories. And the cute little row-house shops catching our attention across the two-laner and beneath the warm glow of street lamps gave way to any eerie notions. We scurried across the road oblivious, more concerned with skirting the continual flow of traffic between one side of the street and the other.

The dank and dark cellar of the orphanage where ghostly children still roam.

Some who visit the building have felt cold spots. Doors bang, clothing is tugged. Pictures taken in the basement have yielded ghostly children and shadows.

When I visited on a tour with Ghostly Images of Gettysburg, we were settled into the cellar of the basement listening to the tour guide relating stories. I felt a tug on the back of my jacket and turned to see if someone was trying to get my attention. I only received a questioning gaze from those behind me as to the reason I was blinking curiously at them. Twice more, there was a tug on my jacket. I turned a little sideways to see if someone was playing a prank. No one moved. But my coat did with two quick jerks. Moments after, a large double-thud rang out on the door leading to the dank cellar. All necks of those attending craned toward the door. There was complete silence before we all turned back to the tour guide as if he might be willing to divulge it was merely the wind outside or another tour guide creating the noise. Only an uncertain gaze was returned!

As part of our tour, we took a short stroll around the neighborhood. While walking in the brisk air, both my daughter and I heard childlike giggles that were certainly not coming from anyone in the group. The night was cold, and few people were outside. Then, where the National Cemetery abuts a parking lot, I watched as two shadowy figures in uniform ran pell-mell straight through the cemetery fence where it was no-mans land during the battle, hunkered down as if trying to avoid detection. I had seen two ghosts!

Outside the Gettysburg National Cemetery where I saw two figures crouch-running as quickly as they could as if trying to sneak from one place to the other without getting shot. 789 Baltimore Street. (39.821797, -77.230526)

Tillie Pierce House Inn
301 Baltimore Street
Gettysburg, PA 17325
39.826773, -77.231297

A Girl's Tale and a Ghostly Soldier

Tillie Pierce—(March 11, 1848—March 15, 1914) At the tender age of 15, she fled town for safety and instead, ended up tending to soldiers at a field hospital where she was staying.

Matilda Jane "Tillie" Pierce was the daughter of one of the town's eight butchers in 1860. She, her parents and her four siblings and several others lived above her father's shop. She was only 15-years-old when soldiers marched past her house just before and during the Battle of Gettysburg. Two of her eldest brothers enlisted in the Union Army.

When the first Confederate troops began to assemble outside town near the Theological Seminary for a raid of goods and horses, she was in school with her sister, Maggie. The children peered out the door to see what she described as a dark, dense mass working their way toward town, and the headteacher immediately sent them home. Tillie rushed to her house, and there, she peeked between the curtains of the family sitting room watching the rebel soldiers in ragged clothing and covered in dirt infiltrate the town shooting, cursing and ransacking for food and horses.

With their looting complete in Gettysburg, the Confederate soldiers left in the same kind of flurry they had come, heading toward York, about 25 miles away. And by Tuesday, June 30th, the Union soldiers began to arrive. Delighted at first, the neighborhood girls ran out to cheer the assemblage on, waving handkerchiefs in the air. Then, as the sound of guns began to ring out during the evening, her parents made plans for Tillie to head outside town with a neighbor and her little children to what they believed a safer area, the remote, rock-strewn Jacob Weikert farm.

Tillie Pierce fleeing the town with a neighbor and her children. From: *At Gettysburg, or, What a girl saw and heard of the battle—*

Around 1:00 in the afternoon of July 1st, they walked up Baltimore Street and through Evergreen Cemetery to what they believed was a sheltered area away from the oncoming storm of guns and cannons.

Little did the Pierce family know they were sending their daughter to a place that would become one of the most battle-ravaged areas—just east of Little Round Top. And the home and barn where she was staying, a large field hospital—over 700 wounded and dying soldiers were housed in the home and barn.

Distraught at the sad state of the bloodied and wounded soldiers coming in, she remarked in her book later of sobbing into her hands. Consoled by the nurses and a chaplain, she fought back her fears and also cared for the wounded. In later years, she would write about her experiences during the battle in a booklet called At Gettysburg, Or What A Girl Saw And Heard Of The Battle—

"Nothing before in my experience had ever paralleled the sight we then and there beheld," she told readers. "There were the groaning and crying, the struggling and dying, crowded side by side, while attendants sought to aid and relieve them as best they could. —To the south of the house, and just outside of the yard, I noticed a pile of limbs higher than the fence. It was a ghastly sight! Gazing upon these, too often the trophies of the amputating bench, I could have no other feeling, than that the whole scene was one of cruel butchery."

The Tillie Pierce House, where she lived on Baltimore Street in Gettysburg, was named for this girl who drew courage from the suffering during the battle. And no doubt, the home she lived in saw much of the struggle and has taken in the energy of those who have lived there too. The sound of whinnying horses has been heard near the home. Impressions of small children are captured on camera—in 2016, a visitor to the inn was taking pictures and caught the image of a boy in Victorian clothing standing on the stairway to the attic.

The home of Tillie Pierce is now an inn and
it is haunted by a soldier.

All of the ghosts that visit the Tillie Pierce Inn
appear as pleasant as any ghosts can be. Even the spirit
of a Union soldier who walks the stairway up and
down during the night does little more than provide a
sound that might scare some who are faint at heart. A
simple fan will muffle the sound. Those trying to sleep
will have to recognize that what the ghost went
through before dying was much more terrorizing than
the soft clatter of boot heels to wood over and over.

Iverson's Pits at
Oak Ridge Observation Tower
Doubleday Avenue
Gettysburg, PA 17325
Tower Overlook:
39.844048, -77.241923
Iverson's Pits:
39.843492, -77.243467

Spirits of Iverson's Pits

Alfred Iverson.

The field called *Iverson's Pits*. It has a chilling story filled with ghosts left over from a disastrous military defeat and a massacre.

His father chose a military career for Alfred Iverson, Jr. to begin at Tuskegee Military Institute. However, Iverson quit so he could fight in the Mexican-American War. Later he would choose a career as a lawyer, but again find himself as a military man—a Confederate general in the American Civil War. But this story isn't about Iverson and his reasonable-at-best profession as a leader up to the Civil War. It is about the 1,350-man

North Carolina brigade in his command during the first day of battle in Gettysburg. While obscuring himself in the rear, he ordered his soldiers across an open field northwest of town in a place called Oak Ridge. The southern men were in tight formation as a support for a more massive Confederate attack on the Union. But they would be slaughtered by an ambush—Union soldiers concealed behind a wall of stone rising from their hiding place and blanketing them in bullets and massacring the soldiers with musket shot at point-blank range.

They toppled like a long line of dominoes set end to end, entire lines falling from a single volley of bullets. Trapped under heavy fire, Iverson saw some soldiers waving white handkerchiefs and others lying prone on the ground. In the heat of the moment, he remarked that his men were cowards, not realizing all those men were either killed or injured. From his vantage point, it appeared they were surrendering.

Nine-hundred brave men were dead or dying that day of battle. The corpses were buried in a mass grave right there on the spot in an area grimly nicknamed Iverson's Pits. Family members who searched for their lost sons and husbands for a proper burial would never be able to identify them from the remains. Iverson suffered a nervous breakdown as he realized the carnage before him and pulled out of his position as unfit for his command. He would later return to minor tasks as an officer until Robert E. Lee removed him from command combat.

The bodies of Iverson's men were exhumed and returned to their homelands in the southern states about seven years after the war. But even long after, as dusk fell on the land of Iverson's Pits where they were first hastily buried, farmhands dropped their tools and refused to work longer for fear of seeing the shadows and hear the ghostly shouts of the long-dead troops. Some of those entering the site had even watched in stunned silence as a spirited rider high-tailed it along an old road.

Looking out toward the fields at dusk where Iverson's men battled and were buried: (39.843350, -77.243297)

Henry Robinson Berkeley, with the Amherst (Virginia) Artillery would describe the horror in his diary:
This morning on getting up, I saw a sight which was perfectly sickening and heart-rending in the extreme. It would have satiated the most blood-thirsty and cruel man on God's earth. There were, [with]in a few feet of us, by actual count, 79 North Carolinians laying dead in a straight line. I stood on their right and looked down their line. It was perfectly dressed. Three had fallen to the front, the rest had fallen backward; yet the feet of all these dead men were in a perfectly straight line. Great God! When will this horrid war stop? This regiment belonged to Iverson's Brigade, and had been pushed forward between two stone fences, behind which the Yankees were laying concealed. They had all evidently been killed by one volley of musketry and they had fallen in their tracks without a single struggle.

Today, the ground where Iverson's men were slaughtered is still known for ghostly activity. Two shadowy soldiers are seen stepping through the cornfields nearby. The blast of battle gunshots ring out low and muffled. And then there are the gentle thuds of long-dead bodies falling to the ground, followed by otherworldly moans sweeping off the grassy clearing.

Doubleday Inn
104 Doubleday Avenue
Gettysburg, PA 17325
39.841314, -77.242594

Front Row Seat to Battlefield Ghosts

The Doubleday Inn —a beautiful bed and breakfast settled deep into the battleground—by Iverson's Pits.

You can't get much closer to the Battle of Gettysburg than the Doubleday Inn. The land is directly within the bounds of Gettysburg National Military Park. The property where the home now stands was once an orchard and the section called Oak Ridge. It would see the better part of the fighting on the first day of the battle. The home was built on the land in 1939 for a minister who traveled many roads to preach in surrounding communities, and it would later become an inn—a haunted inn, that is. Guests have felt gentle touches during their stay and have also seen strange lights illuminating much like a candle outside.

Spangler's Spring
Colgrove Avenue
Gettysburg, PA 17325
39.814484, -77.217228

Pale Mist at Spangler's Spring

Spangler's Spring at the south base of Culp's Hill as it appeared during wartime. *Retrieved: Gettysburg; the Pictures and the Story.*

On the first day of battle, Union troops occupied a meadow including a spring that flowed into Rock Creek on the Spangler family property that was a popular picnic area for locals. It was highly coveted due to its water source—Spangler's bubbling spring. So at nightfall, Confederate units attacked, skirmishing for the positions. Back and forth, the fight would swing until finally, and after the death of many soldiers, the Union troops retook what the rebels sought.

Spangler's Spring today—The stone arch was added in 1895 to cover and protect the water source from the huge number of visitors. Later, due to concerns of water contamination, the water supply was stopped. *Photo: Julie Feinstein.*

Legends have always filtered down from one generation to the next that although the battle raged on the evening of July 2nd, not all enemies fought who came to partake of the fresh, cold water. At times, it was shared by Union or Confederate alike as if a temporary truce had been called at that spot while battling beneath Culp's Hill. In the July 1912 Evening News from Wilkes-Barre, a Lieutenant Johnson of Virginia related to reporters that he, himself, had been one of those soldiers who laid down his gun to the enemy there. In the darkness of night, he had captured a New York Volunteer and took his weapon, but released his prisoner unmolested. As the sun rose the next morning, the men prepared to fight again.

But it is the ghostly figure seen here drawing attention to phantom fare. Some see a pale mist rise near the spring. It forms into a ghostly woman wearing white. It is thought to be a woman from 1880 who committed suicide after being jilted by her love.

Gettysburg College
Pennsylvania Hall
Gettysburg, PA 17325
39.835075, -77.234322

Specters from the Cupola to the Cellar

The cupola above the Gettysburg College where ghostly apparitions are seen.

Within the boundaries of town is a four-year college of liberal arts and sciences. Although most know it as Gettysburg College, it was called Pennsylvania College of Gettysburg during the Civil War and was little more than a few brick buildings for student dorm housing and classrooms. While the war carried on outside its doors, the College's Pennsylvania Hall (also called Old Dorm) was used as an emergency field hospital, a morgue for Confederate and Union soldiers, as a signal post to send messages to the officers, and as a lookout to observe the enemy.

The college in August of 1863. *Library of Congress.*

Now administrative offices fill the building. And ghosts. The cupola above the building provided a high vantage point for following the battle—officers and General Lee, himself, used the building to watch over his men. There were also sentries posted there for safety reasons.

Some of these guards remain. One evening, a student passing beneath the building looked up to see a shadowy figured frantically waving at him. Unsure if it was a call of alarm because someone was stuck in the cupola and locked up there when the building closed for the night, the student yelled upward to advise the figure help was on the way. The form completely vanished!

Campus security was called in to investigate and found no one inside and the front doors securely bolted.

Pennsylvania College, Pennsylvania Hall. Take a walk through campus and look around. You just might meet a ghost from its past during the battle. *Library of Congress.*

Shannon Keeler, Staff Writer Gettysburgion (Gettysburg College) reported an extraordinary story. A secretary working in Penn Hall had taken an elevator to the basement. When the door opened wide, before him, he witnessed a Civil War hospital setup with lights and soldiers and people rushing about before the door shut. It wouldn't be the first or the last time this grisly scene would play out. Mark Nesbitt (*Ghosts of Gettysburg* book series) recounted that two administrators during the 1980s were using the elevator. It went straight to the basement, stopping long enough for the doors to open wide, exposing a hospital room with bloodied patients and doctors hovering above them.

The Abraham Trostle Farm
180 United States Avenue
Gettysburg, PA 17325
39.801954, -77.243022

Ghostly Scent of Death at a Farm

The Trostle Barn- *Photo: Brenda Neuroth-AllVisionsArt*

Abraham and Catherine Trostle lived on this farm, along with their children during the war. However, when the Battle of Gettysburg got too close, they left for a safer place. It was a sound decision. On July 2, 1863, when the fighting was heavy here—Captain John Bigelow was ordered to hold the position of his 9th Massachusetts Battery at the farm no matter what the cost. Union lines on the Emmitsburg Road had been broken, and the Union needed to hold off advancing Confederates from Barksdale and Kershaw's brigades.

The 9th Massachusetts' desperate last stand was unsuccessful. They were overrun and forced to retreat to Cemetery Ridge. In the struggle, the attacking Confederates deliberately shot Union artillery horses so the cannon could not be maneuvered. They lost at least sixteen battery horses and countless soldiers, and yet they still managed to buy time for the Union Army. The farm would become a field hospital for the dying and wounded, and horse carcasses littered the yard.

The Trostle farm right after the battle with dead horses scattered all around. *Library of Congress*

The reek of dead animals—over 116 dead horses—enveloped the area for days. Living on a farm myself, I've taken in rescue horses that are older than the hills and spend out their dying days happily feasting on specially hand-cut alfalfa and home-made molasses feed. But when they finally pass on, their ghastly stench hovers in the air almost immediately dead-deer-on-a-hot-August-highway-style. The lingering stink seeps through closed windows and loiters there. So it is no surprise to me that even now, visitors to the old Trostle Farm have caught the ghostly reek of death and dying—rotten corpses of those poor, long-gone horses.

The George Weikert Farm
United States Avenue
Gettysburg, PA 17325
39.801900, -77.235207

The Dead Have Returned

George Weikert Home. *Photo: Brenda Neuroth-AllVisionsArt*

The George Weikert House is haunted. It was one of several homes belonging to the immediate family of the George Weikert (three of his sons) and a distant cousin. The National Park Service now owns it. It was a field hospital during the fighting, and amputated arms and legs were piled high outside the home's doors. At least six soldiers died within the walls, and when the family returned, the yard was filled with graves. The dead have returned. Former tenants have divulged they heard heavy, pacing footsteps treading over and over in the attic. Doors open and shut on their own—one so much that a worker nailed it shut.

Cashtown Inn
1325 Old Rte 30
Orrtanna, PA 17353
39.884796, -77.360302

Knocks and Noises and a Ghostly Encampment

Cashtown Inn- *Photo: Brenda Neuroth-AllVisionsArt*

Cashtown Inn has been in business to travelers since 1797, getting its name from the owner who, at the time, would only accept cash for his rooms. During the Battle of Gettysburg, Confederates used it as a headquarters and the area as a camp. It would become a field hospital for soldiers. Visitors hear knocking and unexplained noises within the walls and a chair rocks on its own. A full-bodied apparition of a Confederate soldier even walks the halls!

Another story surrounding the area between Cashtown and nearby Hilltown is that of a doctor who was riding by horseback in the blackness of night to visit a patient in the community. Along one of the isolated backroads, he was abducted by a band of Confederate soldiers and forced to return to an encampment in the forest where their wounded battlefield companions hid.

He patched their wounds with what he had available and after some time, was allowed to be on his way. The strange thing about it was that the war had been over for many years. The doctor would return the next morning to the area he had tended to the soldiers. But they were gone and it was as if they had never been there at all!

Baladerry Inn
40 Hospital Road
Gettysburg, PA 17325
39.798070, -77.217154

Accommodating Stay for Guests—including the Ghostly Kind

Baladerry Inn

As accommodating and friendly as the owners of the Baladerry Inn are, it isn't any wonder ghosts have decided to stick around after the Battle of Gettysburg. Seven spirits, to be exact that may be Confederate soldiers buried under the tennis courts near the home. The oldest section of the inn was constructed in 1812 on the Bushman Farm as a tenant home, and the rest of the main house was an addition in 1830. The building was there during the Battle of Gettysburg and became a field hospital for wounded soldiers.

George Spangler Farm
488 Blacksmith Shop Road
Gettysburg, PA 17325
39.801668, -77.221029

A Certain Presence at the Well

Spangler's Farm. *Photo: Brenda Neuroth-AllVisionsArt*

George and Elizabeth Spangler, with their four children, lived on a farm just outside Gettysburg proper. It was a productive family farm, much like many others in America at the time with cows, sheep, horses, and pigs. It also boasted an orchard and a thriving crop.

During the battle, the Spanglers chose to stay in their home even as the farm became a Union artillery staging area, a field hospital occupied by the Eleventh Corps, and a burial ground for nearly 205 soldiers, many who were reinterred later by family.

About 1,800 wounded Union soldiers and 100 wounded Confederate soldiers were cared for here, stuffed in every nook and cranny of the barns, outbuildings, and tents. Some were without cover. Almost all were on bare ground. For five days and some in torrential downpours, doctors tried desperately to save the lives of many on the farm that compared to "a butcher shop"—the number of sawed-off arms and legs piled everywhere. It is even supposed that Confederate General Lewis Armistead was placed in the small summer kitchen at the farm after Pickett's Charge. As a ranking officer, they isolated him from the regular soldiers. He died there.

Spangler's Farm around 1890.

After the war was over, the family and tenants living there told of waking in the middle of the night to sounds outside. Peering through the second-story windows, they would see a figure dressed in white hauling two water buckets, one in each hand.

It would lug the buckets to an old well once there, then turn and walk back toward the house. When one of the family would trudge down the stairway to see if anyone had entered the home, the figure had mysteriously disappeared. And some maintain the apparition remains today, a spirit of the battle hauling buckets of water for eternity to soldiers long dead, back and forth from well to makeshift hospital.

*East Cemetery Hill at the
25th & 75th Ohio
Volunteer Infantry
Regiments Monument
and The Grove*
*Wainwright Avenue
Gettysburg, PA 17325
39.823196, -77.228527*

Ghosts at the Hill. Ghosts at the Grove.

Here along East Cemetery Hill—Great odds and a charge by the famous and feared Louisiana Fierce Tigers would not stop the Ohio Volunteers from prevailing in life—or in death.

At the foot of Cemetery Hill on Wainright Avenue, there's a monument tucked into a little woods and settled beneath the shade from the tree canopy overhead. It commemorates the little known, but incredibly significant, struggle of the 25th and 75th Ohio Volunteers on July 2nd to push back a much larger party of Confederate forces. Just hours before, these very men were almost a mile and a half away in an open field called Blocher's (or Barlow) Knoll when things suddenly took a turn for the worse. Continually, this close-knit group of men were forced to retreat, pushed violently back, and through the town of Gettysburg. The losses were great, with only 27 percent of the men remaining. Those who were still alive withdrew to the safety of a cubby beneath Cemetery Hill.

As darkness came upon them, the worn men positioned themselves behind a jagged line of stone walls along a slope of East Cemetery Hill. Their day had been brutal enough. But as night fell upon them, their real nightmare would begin because they found themselves entertaining a seemingly impossible task— blocking the Louisiana Fierce Tigers, an infantry troop that had the reputation as being one of the fiercest and most dreaded of the Confederate units. This renowned unit had already pushed the corps through the town and on to Cemetery Hill. After the deaths of their comrades, the Ohio soldiers should have been broken. They'd been beaten down again and again. But 25th and 75th Ohio Volunteers were not giving up without a fight yet even as the rebels' roar yelled out.

The area of the charge and where ghosts can be seen. Beyond, a grove of trees with even more legendary ghosts.

They stood their ground as the Confederates broke through Union lines in hand to hand combat under cover of dark and thick gunfire smoke—Louisiana Fierce Tigers had gained quite a reputation as being ferocious (hence their nickname) bounding over the stone wall like deer jumping over a fence row, hitting at them with bayonets, knives, clubbed musket and stones from the wall, a final desperate attempt to stop the onslaught. The Ohio Volunteers prevailed. It was a smashing victory for the Union. Maybe not so much for the men. Their losses were staggering—they arrived at Gettysburg with a force of 220 men. At the end of the day, only 60 remained. At this struggle, they suffered the second-highest losses in the entire Union Army.

This monument marks the fighting area of the 25th and 75th Ohio Volunteers and the Louisiana Fierce Tigers. Nearby, shadows have been seen brushing across the stone walls and rushing forward in eternal battle.

Where these men fell is haunted. The location is on the lower levels of Cemetery Hill along the rock wall and behind Warrior Stadium and the Gettysburg Area Middle School. Visitors walking the road and beside the forest grove feel fingers touching them. Their clothing is pulled. There's a sensation ghost-sensitive people will get—anxiety creeping in the belly or slipping up the spine stopping dead as the hairs on the back of the neck rise. One story passed on to me involved a classroom of students at the nearby middle school.

As the students were hunkered down at their desks one day working hard on a test, unexpectedly, there was a sharp wind sweeping into the room. Right after, the apparition of a Civil War soldier burst through a back wall, running up the aisle between school desks before disappearing into the wall at the front of the classroom!

But these aren't the only ghosts said to tread the area here. Old stories surfaced from the brave men of the Louisiana Fierce Tigers who had battled that day. They may not have succeeded, but they fought bravely, none-the-less—well, except for five men who had led the charge, then seemed to vanish once the hand-to-hand combat began. Deserters, they were. As the soldiers of the Louisiana Fierce Tigers were pushed back by Union troops, they stumbled upon their men hiding behind stones in the forested grove on the opposite side of Wainwright Avenue. No one speaks about what occurred right after, only that the deserters were found murdered, and it was not by enemy guns. Now they haunt the grove. Ghost lights appear amidst the tree in the dark of night and the light of day, and people are pushed and prodded. There have even been forms seen that are darker than the night, moving and swaying in the brush.

The Grove—watch for lights and occasional shadow figures.

Gettysburg National Cemetery
791 Baltimore Street
Gettysburg, PA 17325
39.821214, -77.231856

Spectral Balls of Light

The National Cemetery—the central point of the cemetery and the general area where Lincoln delivered the Gettysburg Address. Spectral balls of lights are seen throughout the cemetery.

Visitors to the cemetery note balls of lights even during the daylight hours (it is closed dusk to dawn) around the cemetery. The best way to catch them is to take lots of pictures. But they have also been seen by the naked eye.

Alumni Park
Site of the Samuel
McCreary House
Intersection of 1 Lefever Street
with Baltimore Street
Gettysburg, PA 17325
39.825398, -77.230954

Ode to William H. Poole

Bullet Holes in Fence, Gettysburg, Pa.

The Samuel McCreary home in the early 1900s. It is no longer there and a pretty park is in its place. Oh, along with a ghost.

The little park at the intersection of Lefever and Baltimore streets was once the site of the family home of 60-year-old brick maker Samuel McCreary and his family. During the battle and when the house was still here, this area was a prime spot for sharpshooters as it sat on the advance Confederate skirmish line. Anyone caught in the open was a possible target. And the home, itself, was occupied by Louisiana Confederate sharpshooters because it faced the Union position on Cemetery Hill.

One of the soldiers posted there was Corporal William H. Poole, 9th Louisiana Regiment, who had pushed a drop leaf table across a balcony doorway facing Cemetery Hill. There, he knelt and proceeded to fire at Union soldiers. Although the table was large enough to cover the door, it was not thick enough to deflect a Minié ball that crashed right through, killing him.

When the family returned to the home, they found the body. They wrapped it in a quilt and carefully buried it in the yard. Now and then, William Poole returns to let folks know he is still around. His ghost walks the property, pausing long enough to look up to the doorway that is no longer there and stare before he fades from sight.

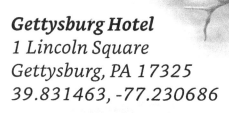

Gettysburg Hotel
1 Lincoln Square
Gettysburg, PA 17325
39.831463, -77.230686

A Hub for Travelers and Ghosts

Gettysburg Hotel—A hub for travelers since 1797, it has collected a few ghosts along the way.

It began as Scott's Tavern in 1797 along one of the busiest intersections in Gettysburg and the stagecoach route. In the 1890s, the Gettysburg Hotel replaced the tavern/inn building. It has been a hub for travelers coming and going from the town since the beginning, and along its way, it has collected a few ghosts from its past. The hotel has a resident spirit dubbed Rachel, possibly a nurse from the time of the Civil War. She tends to rifle through drawers. There have also been sightings of a lady dancing in the ballroom, and a wounded soldier wandering the building.

Inn at Cemetery Hill
613 Baltimore Street
Gettysburg, PA 17325
39.822759, -77.231409

The Warning

Inn at Cemetery Hill—This was one of the stories we learned while taking the Ghostly Images of Gettysburg tours. I do recommend for a hands-on experience, take a ghost tour. Even for skeptics, it is an interesting way of learning local history.

You can't stay much closer to the battlefield than the Inn at Cemetery Hill. Ghosts leftover from the Battle of Gettysburg surround this hotspot hotel. One guest, during her stay at the hotel, awakened to someone dressed in a Civil War military uniform hovering over her bed. She started to rise and felt as if hands were pushing her down. She lay there for what seemed an eternity before she could get up from the bed. Was she frightened? Yes, but unhurt. This strange feeling overcame her—had the ghost been warning her to stay down, worried that if she stood, she would get shot by bullets that had whizzed past this very spot when the North and South battled on Cemetery Hill?

The Field of Pickett's Charge
Virginia Monument Circle
Gettysburg, PA 17325
39.814419, -77.250227

A Strange Incident in an Old Field

Painting of Pickett's Charge, titled "Battle of Gettysburg,"
By Peter Frederick Rothermel.

Pickett's Charge took place on the third day of battle in Gettysburg—July 3, 1863. A day earlier, the Confederates had attacked the Union at Little Round Top, Culp's Hills, and Cemetery Hill. But the Union had the high ground and craggy terrain in their favor and held hard against the attacks. The two armies were two days into the battle and deadlocked—Rebel against Yankee. The Confederate forces fell back, reforming at Seminary Ridge. There, they made plans to penetrate the center of Union forces at Cemetery Ridge with three full divisions of infantry (12,000 to 15,000 men) converging past a copse of trees and into an open field almost ¾ of a mile in length, smashing the center of the Union Army to march onward to Washington.

Photograph (circa1863-1865) shows clump of trees (left) that was point of direction for Pickett's soldiers. *Source: Battles and leaders of the Civil War : being for the most part contributions by Union and Confederate officers : based upon "The Century War series." New York : Century Co., 1887, volume 3, page 388.*

On July 3rd, nearly 15,000 Rebel soldiers advanced up Cemetery Ridge in a last-ditch, go-for-broke endeavor to end the war. Instead, their plan ended disastrously as their leader overshot his target. The Confederate soldiers marched from the trees and across the field with bayonets fixed while being shot and shelled by the Union. They were not to fire or call out until they were directly on top of the enemy, so their march was at a quick and energized pace.

Within a few hundred yards of the lines, Union soldiers switched from exploding shells to the lethal spray of hundreds of round lead balls bursting from canister shot (a metal can the size of a cannon-bore and filled with 50 to 100 lead balls) sent from cannons. It repulsed the attack. In less than one hour, it was nothing less than a slaughterhouse with dead and dying Confederate soldiers strewn across the field.

A gun and gunners that repulsed Pickett's charge at Gettysburg. *Library of Congress*

The 1992 movie Gettysburg was based on the book Killer Angels by Michael Shaara. The initial advance scenes from Pickett's Charge were filmed at the exact location of the battle. Three-thousand extras in Confederate attire were brought in to march toward the Union position and the stone wall; it was about half of the way where they stopped to preserve the well-being of the historical battlefield. They had practiced the run several times in the heat and were preparing for a third for the scene.

Most of the reenactors were tired from sitting around most of the day or practicing the scenes. But on the third take, when the men marched out of the woods at the locale, they would cross where many Confederate soldiers had died that day in 1863. Right then, when they crossed that line, many said later that they felt electrically charged, an inspirational state of urgency and haste enveloping them as they set out with feet quickened to nearly a full run. They kept going across the field, charged the fence, and nearly toppled over tourists standing on the lines watching.

The site of Pickett's Charge today. Confederate soldiers would make a heated march toward the copse of trees beyond in 1863, only to be crushed by the enemy. Many years later, the advance would be imitated by reenactors to make a movie with an eerily fervent reflection, mirroring the past. *Image: Pepperkittstudios*

Some might say that this charge was nothing more than the excitement and elation of reliving the battle. But for those who were a part of the charge, well, they say it was almost spiritual.

Maria Furnace
Iron Springs Road
Fairfield, PA 17320
Beneath Culp Ridge along
Iron Springs Road
(Maria Furnace Mountain)
39.776063, -77.397298 to
39.770840, -77.427146
And beyond . . .

Ghost Hounds on his Heels

Somewhere near Maria Furnace where a young man was murdered for the love of a girl, and ghostly hounds forever chase down the horrible killer .

On the first day of February 1893, 18-year-old Emanuel Monn seemed to vanish off the face of the earth about ten miles from Gettysburg. It was surprising to those who knew him in the tight-net community where almost everyone was related somehow, if not by blood, by marriage that he had not mentioned he was going elsewhere. At the time, he was sharing a small cabin with 34-year-old Henry Heist on the George Reese property at Maria Furnace and just a few hundred feet from the Reese home. The two were cutting out a meager living together as woodchoppers at the time and working for a local farmer by the name of Henry Herring.

Nothing appeared amiss until someone brought up the point of a small incident occurring on the very night he disappeared. It seems Emanuel and Henry had been at a small gathering at the Ann and George Reese home on Wednesday, February 1st. Henry Heist had left early. There had been an argument between Henry and Emanuel. Henry had threatened the Reese daughter, Susanna McCleaf, who was also his step-niece, for flirting playfully with Emanuel. Susanna and Emanuel had been seen holding hands in the kitchen that evening, teasing each other, awkwardly dancing as young folks do. The two had even talked excitedly to Susanna's mother about Emanuel escorting Susanna to visit family on the far side of the mountain near Old Forge in the upcoming week. Henry overheard the conversation. It was noted at the Reese home by witnesses, it angered Henry so greatly that he slapped Susanna hard enough to send her across the room.

It was not long after Henry left the Reese home (and under what circumstances is not entirely known) that Emanuel Monn had headed out with a quick goodbye and that he was going back to the cabin. He seemed cheerful; he was playing his mouth harp happily as he went. That was the last any of his friends and family would see of the young Emanuel alive.

It would be Henry who showed up in Emanuel's place to take Susanna to see her family, stating the young man had left town. During the outing, the two also visited Emanuel's family who lived in the vicinity too, who questioned the story that Emanuel had left without telling anyone. It was within a short time that

Emanuel's father began to ask where the boy had gone, as did the nearby families at Maria Furnace.

Henry was questioned about the man's disappearance by authorities but denied knowing anything at all. It is not surprising. Henry was not new at this game and knew how to play it—he'd already spent time in jail. In 1887, he was found guilty for shooting at another man, assault, and battery and was sentenced to almost three years in prison. In 1891, he received a sentence for nearly a year for larceny and petty theft. He would never confess or offer clues to incriminate himself. However, he would sell the cabin and all inside, including an ax and blanket belonging to Emanuel Monn. He would come up with a few feeble stories, excuses for the boy's disappearance—one even included blaming George Reese, stating Emanuel and George had fought, and Henry had discovered the body with George hovering over it. Henry had even gone as far as describing George Reese trying to cut off the boy's head because it wouldn't fit in the scanty hole he had dug in the frozen ground.

On March 12th and after a search along the hillside of Reese's property, Emanuel's body was found 2,185 feet from the cabin in a shallow grave, a pile of brush, flat rocks, and logs overtop. A little digging exposed the toe of a boot sticking out and then Emanuel lying on his back. His skull was crushed in the forehead by a hatchet or hammer, and there was a cut to the throat 3 ½ inches long which appeared to have been made with a hatchet while the head was pulled back. A significant wound lay at the back of the left ear looking as if made by a succession of blows going deep into the brain. Emanuel's windpipe was severed, and his chin partially cutaway.

Henry's victim, young Emanuel, was buried in the old Forge Cemetery in Franklin County. Henry took off down the road with a posse hot on his heels complete with baying hounds—through Tomstown and Mont Alto and beyond. He was nearly caught in Graffenburg. He was able to elude the law for almost two months hiding with family near Germantown, but finally turned himself in to authorities in Gettysburg, Henry was hanged at Gettysburg on January 17, 1894. The conviction of Henry Heist was based entirely on circumstantial evidence—his jealousy of Emanuel's relationship with Susanna. Nobody came forward to claim his body after hanging, not even his parents. He was buried in the potter's cemetery at the county home. On the stone is a simple name and date, and below, the word *Hung*. Rumors quickly spread that his body was stolen, but the grave was opened, and the casket and body were still there.

Henry Heist was the last man hanged in Adams County, in Gettysburg. He may be dead, but his ghost lives on. On cold winter nights, he is seen running along the roads of old Maria Furnace and all the deep and dark cubby holes through South Mountain, forever evading the men who hunted him down. At his heels are the hounds, bounding after him baying long and hard in the air.

Walking Tour Map

Here's a short walking tour with the most prominent
ghostly sites in town. Please use common sense and follow
pedestrian traffic safety laws. Road patterns, traffic
conditions, and crosswalks may change as does
property ownership. 1.5 –3 hours

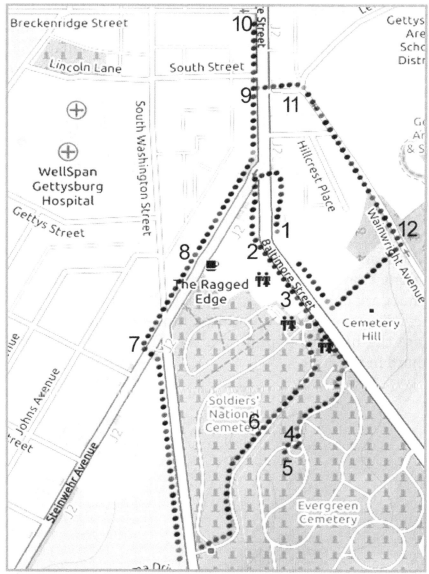

Map Image: openstreetmap.org
Google Map Directions:

(https://tinyurl.com/GettysburgGhostWalkingTour)

1) Jennie Wade House
548 Baltimore Street, Gettysburg, PA 17325

---

2) Inn at Cemetery Hill
use 531 Baltimore Street, Gettysburg, PA 17325

---

3) Orphanage
777 Baltimore Street, Gettysburg, PA 17325

---

4) Jennie Wade Grave—Evergreen Cemetery
(39.819699, -77.230334)

---

5) Jack Skelly's Grave – Evergreen Cemetery
(39.819132, -77.230706)

---

6) Gettysburg National Cemetery
(39.819842, -77.231264)

---

7) Reynold's Death House
237 Steinwehr Avenue Gettysburg, PA 17325

---

8) Dobbin House
89 Steinwehr Ave Gettysburg, PA 17325

---

9) Farnsworth House Inn
401 Baltimore Street, Gettysburg, PA 17325

---

10) Tillie Pierce House Inn
301 Baltimore Street, Gettysburg, PA 17325

---

11) Site of McCreary Home
Alumni Park, 37 Lefever Street, Gettysburg, PA 17325

---

12) 25th & 75th Ohio Volunteer Infantry Regiments and The Grove (39.823196, -77.228527)
Wainwright Avenue , Gettysburg, PA 17325
Walk Cemetery Hill back to Jennie Wade House.

Driving Tour Map

Here's a driving tour with the most prominent ghostly sites around Gettysburg. Please use common sense and follow traffic safety laws. Road patterns, traffic conditions, and parking facilities may change as does property ownership.
1.5 –3 hours

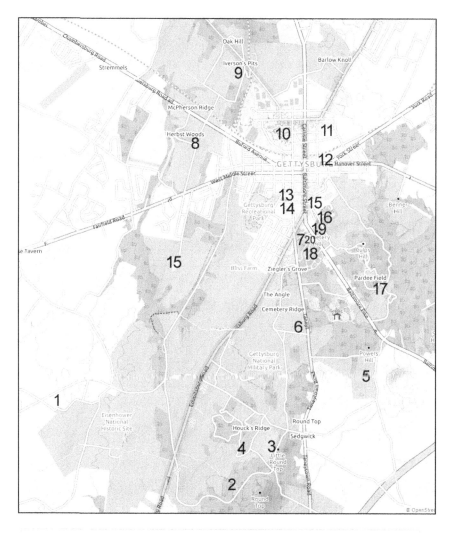

Map Image: openstreetmap.org
Google Map Directions:
(https://tinyurl.com/GettysburgGhostsDrivingTour)

1) **Sachs Covered Bridge**, Waterworks Rd, Gettysburg, PA 17325 (39.797284, -77.276452)
2) **Elon Farnsworth Fell Near this Monument**, Slyder Farm Lane, Gettysburg, PA 17325 (39.786903, -77.243786)
3) **Little Round Top**, Sykes Ave, Gettysburg, PA 17325 (39.791703, -77.237024)
4) **Devil's Den**, Sickles Ave Gettysburg, PA 17325 (39.791289, -77.242338)
5) **George Spangler Farm** 488 Blacksmith Shop Rd Gettysburg, PA 17325 (39.801174, -77.218385)
6) **The Jacob Hummelbaugh Farm** Pleasonton Ave, Gettysburg, PA 17325 (39.808362, -77.231472)
7) **Gettysburg National Cemetery**, 1195 Baltimore Pike, Gettysburg, PA 17325 PA 17325 (39.821362, -77.231852)
8) **Major Gen. Reynolds monument** 55 Reynolds Ave S, Gettysburg, PA 17325 (39.834444, -77.251189)
9) **Iverson's Pits—Oak Ridge Observation Tower** Doubleday Ave, Gettysburg, PA 17325 (39.844034, -77.241769)
10) **Pennsylvania Hall,** Penn Hall Drive Gettysburg, PA 17325 (39.834980, -77.234173)
11) **Brickyard Fight and Coster Avenue Mural**, Coster Ave, Gettysburg, PA 17325 (39.835144, -77.227498)
12) **Where Amos Humiston was found after Brickyard Fight** 35 N Stratton Gettysburg, PA 17325 (39.832046, -77.228717)
13) **Tillie Pierce House Inn**, 301 Baltimore St, Gettysburg, PA 17325 (39.826735, -77.231280) *Across the street is Mark Nesbitt's Ghostly Candlelight Tours.*
14) **Farnsworth House**, 401 Baltimore St, Gettysburg, PA 17325 (39.825634, -77.231352) *At Location: Sleepy Hollow of Gettysburg Candlelight Tours*
15) **Alumni Park** (Site of long-gone McCreary House) 37 Lefever Street, Gettysburg, PA 17325 (39.825395, -77.230336)
16) **25th & 75th Ohio Volunteer Infantry Regiments and The Grove**, Wainwright Ave, Gettysburg, PA 17325 (39.823161, -77.228581)
17) **Spangler's Spring**, Colgrove Ave, Gettysburg, PA 17325 (39.814499, -77.217373)
18) **Evergreen Cemetery, Graves of Jennie Wade and Jack Skelly** 799 Baltimore St, Gettysburg, PA 17325 (39.819695, -77.230386)
19) **Jennie Wade House** 548 Baltimore St, Gettysburg, PA 17325 (39.823330, -77.230646) and
20) **Children's Orphanage across the street**, 777 Baltimore St Gettysburg, PA 17325 (39.822472, -77.230749)

Citations for Stories:

Jennie Wade:
—Bloom, R. (1992). *A History of Adams County, Pennsylvania, 1700-1990.*
—Jennie Wade House | Gettysburg, Pennsylvania. http://www.jennie-wade-house.com/
—Sgt George Boone (1825-1907) - Find A Grave Memorial. https://www.findagrave.com/memorial/36416985/george-boone
—Civil War Facts. (2018, April 23). Retrieved from https://www.battlefields.org/learn/articles/civil-war-facts
—The Civil War. (n.d.). Retrieved from https://www.pbs.org/kenburns/civil-war/war/war-overview/
—The Myths of Gettysburg. (n.d.). Retrieved from https://ehistory.osu.edu/articles/myths-gettysburg
—The Boston Globe Sep 1, 1981 The Ghosts of Gettysburg, Murphy, J
—https://www.railstotrails.org/trailblog/2013/november/12/history-happened-here-a-journey-to-gettysburg/
—Alleman, Mrs. Tillie (Pierce). At Gettysburg, or What a Girl Saw and Heard of the Battle: A True Narrative. New York: W. Lake Borland, 1889.
—Johnston, J. (1917). *The True Story of "Jennie" Wade: A Gettysburg Maid.*
—gettysburgdaily.com/mcclellan-house-jennie-wade-house-battle-damage/
—Wolfe, B. Culp's Hill and Wesley Culp (1839–1863). (2012, June 4). In *Encyclopedia Virginia.* Retrieved from www.EncyclopediaVirginia.org/Culp_s_Hill_and_Wesley_Culp_1839-1863.
—Bellamy, Jeff- Research Support Branch at the National Archives at College Park, Maryland. (n.d.). Brother V Friend Against Friend - A Story of Family, Friendship, Love, and War. Retrieved from https://www.archives.gov/files/publications/prologue/2013/spring/gettysburg.pdf
—Johnston Hastings Skelly war info: https://www.nps.gov/civilwar/search-battle-units-detail.htm?battleUnitCode=UPA0087RI
—Culp Family at Gettysburg. (n.d.). Retrieved from http://www.gdg.org/Gettysburg%20Magazine/culpbros.html
—https://www.hmdb.org/marker.asp?marker=8169
—https://www.thehistorygirl.com/2013/08/the-tragedy-of-jennie-wade.html
—https://auburnpub.com/lifestyles/sayles-the-story-of-three-gettysburg-childhood-friends/article_f36e3cae-4a18-575c-8aaf-8e807f7ee6e8.html
—The Most Glorious Fourth: Vicksburg and Gettysburg, July 4, 1863 By Duane Schultz
—https://www.forensicmag.com/news/2019/03/historys-revolving-door-forensic-interpretation-slaying-mary-virginia-wade-gettysburg
Top of Form

Sauck's Covered Bridge:
—"Historic bridge to close". The Gettysburg Times. May 10, 1968. p. 1. Retrieved December 7, 2010.
—https://todays1019.radio.com/blogs/diane-lyn/haunted-gettysburg-sachs-covered-bridge
—https://npgallery.nps.gov/AssetDetail/NRIS/80003395

Little Round Top:
—**Fighting Regiments of War of Rights - 1st Texas "Ragged Old First"- https://www.youtube.com/watch?v=WSPDQ1h0zSU**
—https://thoughtcatalog.com/jeremy-london/2019/05/14-creepy-incidents-that-happened-at-the-gettysburg-battlefield/
—https://www.liveabout.com/ghost-encounters-at-gettysburg-2594202
—https://monstermovies.fandom.com/wiki/Gettysburg_Ghosts
Aliens and the Antichrist: Unveiling the End Times Deception By John Milor

Devil's Den:
—Quotes from Mark Nesbitt. (2019, August 27). The Ghosts of Gettysburg's Devil's Den. Retrieved from https://history.howstuffworks.com/american-civil-war/devils-den.htm

—https://www.youtube.com/watch?v=S6ErKxIHibk
—https://www.historynet.com/devils-den-gettysburg
__Mark Nesbitt, owner Ghosts of Gettysburg Candlelight Walking Tours and author of Gettysburg ghost books. If you want a whole lot of ghost stories from the area, suggested readings are in his series: Ghosts of Gettysburg: Spirits, Apparitions and Haunted Places on the Battlefield.
—Staged soldiers: https://civilwartalk.com/threads/the-weaver-photographs-at-gettysburg-nov-1863.83786/

John F. Reynolds:
—http://weekinweird.com/2013/12/03/untitled-gettysburg-ghost-hunter-story/
—https://www.battlefields.org/learn/biographies/john-f-reynolds
—https://4girlsandaghost.wordpress.com/2011/02/14/star-crossed-loves-of-gettysburg/
—https://www.findagrave.com/memorial/11784763/catharine_kate_-mary-hewitt

Dobbin House:
—http://www.dobbinhouse.com/history.htm
—Tour: Gettysburg Orphanage Tour. Guide: Jim. -https://www.gettysburgbattlefieldtours.com/ghost-tours/walking-tours/haunted-orphanage-tour/

William Barksdale
—William Barksdale (1821-1863) - Find A Grave Memorial. https://www.findagrave.com/memorial/9855/william-barksdale
—GHOSTS OF GETTYSBURG — American Hauntings. (n.d.). Retrieved from https://www.americanhauntingsink.com/gettysburg
—Jacob Hummelbaugh Farm House - Gettysburg, PA - Ghosts and Hauntings on Waymarking.com. (n.d.). Retrieved from https://www.waymarking.com/waymarks/WMGT2D_Jacob_Hummelbaugh_Farm_House_Gettysburg_PA
—The Most Infamous Floor Brawl in the History of the U.S. House of Representatives. (2014, February 6). Retrieved from https://history.house.gov/Historical-Highlights/1851-1900/The-most-infamous-floor-brawl-in-the-history-of-the-U-S--House-of-Representatives/

Elon Farnsworth:
—https://civilwartalk.com/threads/farnsworth-inn-haunting-and-others.99604/
—Jr, J. C. (2010). Ghost Hunters Reference Guide: Gettysburg Battlefield. Morrisville, NC: Lulu.com.
:—BRIG. GEN. ELON J. FARNSWORTH. (n.d.). Retrieved from http://www.gdg.org/Research/OOB/Union/July1-3/efarnswo.html
—Brigadier General Elon J. Farnsworth. (2016, November 18). Retrieved from https://ss.sites.mtu.edu/mhugl/2016/11/18/brigadier-general-elon-j-farnsworth-2/
—Brueski, Tony. (2018, April 26). The Historic Farnsworth House Inn. Retrieved from http://www.thegravetalks.com/the-historic-farnsworth-house-inn/
—Elon John Farnsworth (1837-1863)... (n.d.). Retrieved from https://www.findagrave.com/memorial/5842062/elon-john-farnsworth
—Loeffel, Bernadette. (n.d.). Gettysburg's Haunted Address - Spirits of Farnsworth House Inn.
—Rantings of a Civil War Historian » Details on the death and burial of Elon Farnsworth. (2015, January 4). Retrieved from http://civilwarcavalry.com/?p=4065
—http://www.gdg.org/Research/OOB/Union/July1-3/efarnswo.html
—http://civilwarcavalry.com/?p=4065
—https://ss.sites.mtu.edu/mhugl/2016/11/18/brigadier-general-elon-j-farnsworth-2/
—https://www.findagrave.com/memorial/5842062/elon-john-farnsworth

Washington's Ghost
—The Times Leader, November 24, 1996 Little Hill Vaults into —History Schogol, Marc Schogol, Jeffrey

—Hearst's Magazine, Volume 23, Issues 4-6
—The_Gettysburg Times Oct_31__1988 Ghost Stories
—Trostle, Kevin, Times Correspondent. (1988, October 31). Ghosts of the Civil War. The Gettysburg Times [Gettysburg], p. 6B.
Hummelbaugh House:
—(1994, October 28). The Gettysburg Times.
—He Still Seeks His Master At Gettysburg. (2018, May 2). Retrieved from https://thewildstare.com/he-still-seeks-his-master-at-gettysburg/
—Hess, S. (2017). America's Political Dynasties. London, England: Routledge.
—I've Scalped Him?US House of Representatives: History, Art & Archives. (n.d.). Retrieved from https://history.house.gov/Blog/Detail/15032401365
The Orphanage:
—https://www.gettysburgbattlefieldtours.com/ghost-tours/walking-tours/haunted-orphanage-tour/
—The Gettysburg Times (Gettysburg, Pa) June 12, 1993
—The Gettysburg Times (Gettysburg, Pa) May 27 2002
—The Gettysburg Times (Gettysburg, Pa) June 19, 1941
—The Gettysburg Times (Gettysburg, Pa) May 9, 1994
—http://civilwarintheeast.com/us-regiments-batteries/new-york-infantry/154th-new-york/
—https://www.historynet.com/desperate-stand-brickyard-fight-gettysburg.htm
—www.youtube.com/watch?v=zbxammYYd4Q
—gettysburgbrickyard.wordpress.com/
—web.archive.org/web/20080316115834/http://—www.historynet.com/wars_conflicts/american_civil_war/3026901.html
—Gettysburg's Unknown Soldier: The Life, Death, and Celebrity of Amos Humiston By Mark H. Dunkelman
—https://markvnesbitt.wordpress.com/2019/08/14/hidden-haunted-hotspots-of-gettysburg/
—https://walkingamongtheghostsofgettysburg.wordpress.com/tag/the-grove-in-gettysburg/
Tillie Pierce House and the Weikert House:
—https://www.americanhauntingsink.com/gettysburg
Tillie Peirce:
—Alleman, Mrs. Tillie (Pierce). At Gettysburg, or What a Girl Saw and Heard of the Battle: A True Narrative. New York: W. Lake Borland, 1889.
—Matilda J. "Tillie" Pierce Alleman, James Pierce, Margaret A. (McCurdy) Pierce, James Shaw Pierce, William Henry Harrison Pierce, and Maggie Pierce. Find A Grave:
—https://www.gettysburgdaily.com/sweney-house-farnsworth-house-christmas-decorations/
Doubleday Inn/Iverson's Pits:
—Alfred Iverson, Jr (1829-1911)... (n.d.). Retrieved from https://www.findagrave.com/memorial/4141/alfred-iverson
—Ghosts Stories - MHN Explores Some of History's Most Haunted Battlefields. (2019, October 27). Retrieved from https://militaryhistorynow.com/2015/10/27/ghosts-stories-mhn-explores-10-of-historys-most-haunted-battlefields/
—Powell, L. (2013, June 21). '79 North Carolinians, their dead feet perfectly aligned' « North Carolina Miscellany. Retrieved from —https://blogs.lib.unc.edu/ncm/index.php/2013/06/21/gettysburg/
—Powell, L. (2013, June 21). '79 North Carolinians, their dead feet perfectly aligned' « North Carolina Miscellany. Retrieved from https://blogs.lib.unc.edu/ncm/index.php/2013/06/21/gettysburg/
—Berkeley, H. R. (1961). Four Years in the Confederate Artillery; The Diary of Private Henry Robinson Berkeley. Edited by William H. Runge.
Spangler's Spring:
—(1911) Gettysburg; the Pictures and the Story. Gettysburg, Pa. Tipton & Blocher. [Pdf] Retrieved from the Library of Congress, https://www.loc.gov/item/unk82029629/

—Trostle, Kevin, Times Correspondent. (1988, October 31). Ghosts of the Civil War. The Gettysburg Times [Gettysburg], p. 6B.
Gettysburg College:
—https://www.americanhauntingsink.com/gettysburg
—https://gettysburgisfun.wordpress.com/2011/10/14/why-pennsylvania-hall-at-gettysburg-college-is-haunted/
—https://gettysburgian.com/2014/11/haunted-g-burg-the-paranormal-pervades-campus/
—Nesbitt, M. (1991). Ghosts of Gettysburg: Spirits, Apparitions and Haunted Places of the Battlefield. Thomas Publications (PA).
Trostle's Farm:
—July 2, 1863: The Second Day at Gettysburg. (n.d.). Retrieved from https://john-fenzel.mykajabi.com/blog/GettysburgSecondDay
—Then And Now Pictures of the Battlefield. (2019, August 13). Retrieved from https://www.nps.gov/gett/learn/photosmultimedia/then-and-now.htm
—The Trostle farm on the Gettysburg battlefield. (2015, February 7). Retrieved from http://gettysburg.stonesentinels.com/battlefield-farms/trostle-farm/
George Weikert Farm:
—http://gettysburg.stonesentinels.com/battlefield-farms/weikert-farm/
—Newman, R. (2017). *Ghosts of the Civil War: Exploring the Paranormal History of America's Deadliest War.* Woodbury, MN: Llewellyn Worldwide.
—https://civilwarwiki.net/wiki/George_Weickert_Farm_(Gettysburg)
Cashtown Inn:
—http://www.cashtowninn.com/pages/history.html
—Gettysburg Times - Oct 31, 1988. Kevin Trostle, Times Correspondent. *Ghosts of the Civil War—The Doctor's Ghostly Patients*
Baladerry Inn:
—Baladerry Inn - About the Inn. https://baladerryinn.com/about_inn/
—**Spangler Farm:**
—Gettysburg Times - Oct 31, 1988. Kevin Trostle, Times Correspondent. Ghosts of the Civil War—Water Buckets
—http://celebrategettysburg.com/livelihood-lost-the-george-spangler-family/
The Grove:
—https://www.gettysburgbattlefieldtours.com/night-of-courage-night-of-cowards/
—https://www.pennlive.com/life-and-culture/erry-2018/10/248e07876b8037/ghosts-of-gettysburg-the-10-mo.html
—-https://www.tripadvisor.com/Attraction_Review-g60798-d3781177-Reviews-After_Dark_Investigations-Gettysburg_Pennsylvania.html#REVIEWS
Pickett's Charge:
—Lancaster New Era April 22, 1993 Lindeman, Katherine. Pickett's Charge. It's Important
—https://militaryhistorynow.com/2016/06/03/the-killing-field-12-remarkable-facts-about-picketts-charge/
McCreary Property/Alumni Park
—Gettysburg Battlefield Tours. (2019, November 6). Raising Your Spirits. Retrieved from https://www.gettysburgbattlefieldtours.com/raising-your-spirits/
—"if anyone showed himself..." - Gettysburg, PA - Signs of History on — Waymarking.com. (n.d.). Retrieved from https://www.waymarking.com/waymarks/—wmHEXC_if_anyone_showed_himself_Gettysburg_PA
—Pfanz, H. W. (2011). Gettysburg--Culp's Hill and Cemetery Hill. Chapel Hill, NC: UNC Press Books.

Gettysburg Hotel:
—Gettysburg Hotel, Est.1797. (n.d.). Retrieved from https://
www.historichotels.org/hotels-resorts/the-gettysburg-hotel-est1797
—Home. (2019, December 30). Retrieved from https://
www.hotelgettysburg.com/
Maria Furnace:
—The Gettysburg Times November 12, 1926 - Page 1
—The Evening Sun Hanover, Pennsylvania October 23, 1990 - Page 47
—Standard-Sentinel Hazleton, Pennsylvania September 04, 1893 - Page 3
—The Gettysburg Times October 24, 1959 - Page 4
—The Gettysburg Times October 17, 1959 - Page 6
—https://www.findagrave.com/memorial/59419381/emanuel-mohn
—https://www.therecordherald.com/article/20130104/
news/130109953
—The Shippensburg News September 08, 1893 - Page 2

Made in the USA
Monee, IL
17 September 2020

42790213R00069